GEORGE GAMOW, *1904*

The Atom

and

Its Nucleus

A SPECTRUM  BOOK

Prentice-Hall, Inc.

Current printing (last digit):

14 13 12 11 10 9 8 7 6 **5**

Preface

Some of the contents of this volume on the structure of the atom and its nucleus are from the author's much larger book, *Matter, Earth and Sky*. There is a considerable amount of added text, especially in the sections on nuclear physics and elementary particles.

G. GAMOW

Contents

Contents

1. The Atom in Philosophy and Chemistry

The Greek Idea

The ancient Greek philosophers who speculated about the nature of things suspected that *the immense variety of different substances forming the world results from a combination of comparatively few simple elements.* Democritus (fifth century B.C.) believed that there are four elementary substances: air, water, stone, and fire, all formed by a very large number of very small particles called *atoms*, i.e., "indivisibles" in Greek. The atoms of air were supposed to carry the properties of "lightness" and "dryness," the atoms of water the properties of "heaviness" and "wetness," the atoms of stone the properties of "heaviness" and "dryness," while the atoms of fire were supposed to be very mobile, "slippery, and hot." On the basis of these ideas, the Greek philosophers attempted to explain the various transformations of matter as resulting from the reshuffling of the atoms constituting matter. They believed that the material of a growing plant is composed of water and stone atoms provided by the soil and atoms of fire supplied by the rays of the sun. In modern chemical terminology, the Greek formula for wood would be SWF. The drying of wood was considered to be the escape from the wood of water atoms, $SWF \rightarrow SF + W$, and the burning of wood the decomposition of dry wood into fire atoms (flame) and stone atoms (ashes), $SF \rightarrow F + S$. Metals were considered to be the combination of stone atoms with varying amounts of fire atoms, SF_n (the fire atoms were supposedly responsible for metallic glitter). Iron was supposed to be rather poor in fire atoms, but gold was considerd to have the maximum amount of them. The formation of metals from ores treated in a furnace was thought to result from the union of the stone atoms of the ore and the fire

1

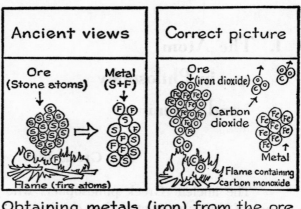

Obtaining metals (iron) from the ore

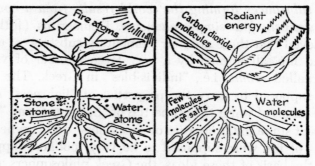

Growing of a plant

FIG. 1. *Two wrong vs. two correct views in chemistry.*

atoms of the flame, $S + nF \rightarrow SF_n$, and it seemed logical to expect that by enriching common metals like iron or copper with fire atoms one should be able to turn them into gold. This point of view, which also prevailed in the Middle Ages, explains the incessant efforts of medieval alchemists to transform common metals into the precious ones.

We know now that these views were quite wrong. The metals themselves and not their ores are elementary substances, and the process that takes place in blast furnaces does not add fire atoms to stony ores and turn them into metals but, quite on the contrary, subtracts oxygen from metallic oxides (ores) and thus liberates pure metals. Also, the material of a growing plant is obtained by the carbon dioxide (carbon + oxygen) from the air combining with the water (hydrogen + oxygen) from the soil, while the sun's rays supply only the energy necessary for synthesizing complex organic substances from these simple ingredients. The difference between the ancient and the modern view in chemistry is shown in Fig. 1. Although the attempted explanations were completely wrong, the idea of reducing the multitude of chemical substances to combinations of comparatively small numbers of simple elements was basically correct and now lies at the foundation of modern chemistry.

Atomic Weights and Valency

The most important fact concerning the formation of various chemical compounds from elements is contained in the so-called law of constant proportions, which states that *the relative amounts of different chemical elements needed to form a definite chemical compound always stand in a certain given ratio.* Thus, when we place a mixture of hydrogen and oxygen gases in a thick-walled container and ignite the gases with an electric spark, we produce a rather violent chemical reaction (or explosion) which results in the formation of water. If the original proportions of hydrogen and oxygen are 1:8 by weight, the reaction will be complete and there will be nothing left over of either of the two gases. If, however, there is originally more hydrogen or more oxygen than is specified in the 1:8 proportion, then a corresponding excess of either gas will be left over. (There exists, however, another compound of hydrogen and oxygen known as *hydrogen peroxide* in which the ratio of the two elements is 1:16.)

The law of constant proportions was interpreted by the British chemist, John Dalton (1766–1844), as being due to atom-to-atom union in the formation of chemical compounds. To explain the above-described facts concerning water and hydrogen peroxide, one can assume that the weight ratio of the atoms of hydrogen and oxygen is 1:16 and that there is one atom of hydrogen per each atom of oxygen in hydrogen peroxide, while there are two hydrogen atoms per each oxygen atom in the case of water. Therefore, writing H for a hydrogen atom and O for an oxygen atom and using a subindex to denote the number of atoms of each kind, we can express the chemical composition of these two substances as:

$$\text{water molecule} = H_2O$$
$$\text{hydrogen peroxide molecule} = HO \quad (\text{or } H_2O_2, \text{ as it can be shown to be by other methods})$$

The second way of writing the expression for hydrogen peroxide indicates that this molecule has one oxygen atom too many in comparison with the much more common compound, water. And, indeed, hydrogen peroxide is an unstable substance that decomposes spontaneously according to the equation:

$$H_2O_2 \rightarrow H_2O + O$$

The free oxygen atoms that are liberated in this reaction possess strong oxidative properties, which make H_2O_2 useful in various bleaching processes, not the least of which is the turning of a dark-haired girl into a platinum blonde.

Similarly, the union of carbon and oxygen may result either in carbon dioxide, CO_2, or, in the case of burning with an unsufficient supply of oxygen, in carbon monoxide, CO. In contrast to hydrogen peroxide, CO molecules lack one oxygen atom and are anxious to rob that extra oxygen atom from any other molecule which does not hold it strongly enough. The ratio by weight of carbon to oxygen in carbon monoxide is 3:4, which can also be written as 12:16. Since the atomic weight of oxygen was established as 16 (i.e., it weighs 16 times as much as a hydrogen atom, which for the present we can consider to be of unit weight), the atomic weight of carbon must be 12. Carbon also unites with hydrogen, giving rise to a gas known as *methane* or "marsh gas." The ratio of hydrogen to carbon in methane is 1:3 or 4:12, and, since 12 is the weight of one carbon atom, the formula of methane must be CH_4. Let us now consider a slightly more complicated example presented by an analysis of ethyl alcohol, which is 52.2 per cent carbon, 34.8 per cent oxygen, and 13.0 per cent hydrogen. By noticing that the ratio $\frac{52.2}{34.8}$ is 1.50, whereas the ratio of the atomic weights of carbon and oxygen is only 0.75, we can conclude that there must be two carbon atoms for each oxygen atom. If there were only one hydrogen atom for each oxygen atom, the ratio of corresponding percentages would have to be $\frac{1}{16} = 0.0625$, but the ratio is actually $\frac{13.0}{34.8} = 0.375$, i.e., six times larger. Therefore there must be six hydrogen atoms per oxygen atom, and the formula for ethyl alcohol is C_2OH_6.

The ability of atoms to unite with one or more other atoms is known as *chemical valency* and can be represented in an elementary way by drawing on each atom a number of hooks that can be coupled with the hooks of other atoms. In the examples so far considered, we have ascribed to hydrogen atoms a valency of 1, to oxygen 2, and to carbon 4. The way atoms are then bound into molecules (the so-called structural formula of the molecule) is shown in Table 1.

Valence "hooks" can also act between identical atoms and bind

TABLE 1

MOLECULAR STRUCTURE OF VARIOUS COMPOUNDS

Water		H—O—H
Hydrogen peroxide		H—O—O—H
Carbon dioxide		O=C=O
Carbon monoxide		=C=O
Methane		H—C—H (with H above and H below)
Ethyl alcohol		H—C—C—O—H (with H above and below each C)
Hydrogen gas		H—H
Oxygen gas		O=O
Ozone		O—O—O triangle

them into "diatomic" or "triatomic" molecules of a simple chemical substance, as indicated in the last three items of Table 1. Similar relations can be found for other chemical elements and for more complicated chemical compounds.

In speaking about chemical valency, we must mention six very peculiar elements: argon, helium, krypton, neon, radon, and xenon. These do not possess any chemical valency whatsoever. The atoms of these elements despise any chemical intimacy and prefer to remain alone; they do not even form pairs between themselves as other atoms often do, so their molecules are always "monatomic." Closely connected with this chemical inertness is the fact that all these six substances are gases and liquefy only at very low temperatures. Using the self-apparent analogy, we call these elements *noble gases* or, sometimes, *rare gases,* since, indeed, they all are rather rare on the earth. As everbody knows, helium is used for filling balloons and dirigibles to avoid fires, and neon, which emits a brilliant red light when subjected to an electric discharge, is used for making luminous signs for advertising.

The Periodic Law

Although the arrangement of chemical elements in alphabetical order is convenient for inventory purposes, it is more reasonable to arrange them in the order of increasing atomic weights. In doing so, we find rather remarkable regularities which have led chemists to a rational classification of the elements. Arranging the elements in order of increasing atomic weights,* we obtain the following sequence: H, *He*, Li, Be, B, C, N, O, F, *Ne*, Na, Mg, Al, Si, P, S, Cl, *A*, K, Ca, Sc, Ti, V, Cr, Mn, Fe, Co, Ni, Cu, Zn, Ga, Ge, As, Se, Br, *Kr*, Rb, Sr, Y, Zr, Nb, Mo, Tc, Ru, Rh, Pd, Ag, Cd, In, Sn, Sb, Te, I, *Xe*, Cs, Ba, La, etc. We notice, first of all, that there is a remarkable regularity in the distribution of noble gases, shown in *italics*, through the sequence: there is only 1 element preceding *He*, 7 elements between *He* and *Ne*, another 7 elements between *Ne* and *A*, 17 elements between *A* and *Kr*, and another 17 elements between *Kr*

---

* The careful student will notice that K, Ni, and I are out of order, but, as it was found later, the sequence of chemical properties has priority over atomic weights.

and *Xe*. Finally, there are 31 elements between *Xe* and *Rn*, which is the heaviest known noble gas.

The elements immediately following the noble gases, lithium, sodium, potassium, rubidium, and cesium, are physically and chemically very similar to each other. They are all light, silvery-white metals with high chemical activity. If we drop a small piece of any of these elements in water, it will undergo a violent chemical reaction of the type:

$$Li + H_2O \longrightarrow LiOH + H$$
$$Na + H_2O \longrightarrow NaOH + H$$
etc.

liberating hydrogen and forming the corresponding "hydroxide" with water (structural formula, Li—O—H, etc.). The hydrogen liberated in this reaction often becomes ignited and produces a flame which takes on the characteristic color of the vaporized metal (yellow for sodium, red for potassium, etc.). Uniting with hydrogen and oxygen, these elements form "hydrates" and "oxides" of the type LiH (Li—H), Li_2O (Li—O—Li), etc., showing that their valency is 1. These elements are commonly known in chemistry as *alkali metals*.

The second neighbors to the right of the noble gases, beryllium, magnesium, calcium, strontium, barium, and radium, also form a homologous group known as *alkali-earth metals*. As their name indicates, they are similar to the alkali metals, but, as a rule, they are much harder and less reactive. Reacting with water, they produce compounds of the type $Ca(OH)_2$ (H—O—Ca—O—H), while uniting with hydrogen and oxygen they give rise to compounds such as CaH_2(H—Ca—H) and CaO (Ca=O), which indicates that their valency is 2. Similarly, we find that the third group to the right, boron, aluminum, etc., possesses a valency of 3 as demonstrated by such compounds as boron oxide, B_2O_3(O=B—O—B=O), and aluminum hydroxide, $Al(OH)_3$.

Now if we look at the elements standing to the left of the noble gases, we will find that they are very similar to each other, but as different from metals as they could possibly be. This group comprises fluorine, chlorine, bromine, iodine, and astatine, and they are known as the *halogens*. They have a strong affinity for both alkali and alkali-earth metals, with which they form such compounds as NaCl (ordinary table salt) and $CaBr_2$, indicating that they possess a single valency. The second neighbors to the left of the noble gases, oxygen, sulfur, etc., are also in some ways similar to each other and possess a valency of 2.

The existence of homologous groups and of a certain periodicity in the chemical properties of elements arranged in the order of increasing atom weights was noticed by several chemists during the nineteenth century, but the most important step of actually arranging the elements into a periodic table was made in 1869 by the Russian chemist, Dmitri Mendeleev (1834–1907). Mendeleev was handicapped in his studies because in his time the list of known chemical elements was rather incomplete and, in particular, the existence of the noble gases was not even suspected. From the sequence given above, Sc, Ga, Ge, Tc, and Rh were missing, making the sequence quite irregular except for the first two periods. Driven by a deep belief that there *must be* a regular periodicity in the natural sequence of elements, Mendeleev made the bold hypothesis that the deviations from the expected periodicity in his list were due to the failure of contemporary chemistry to have discovered some of the elements existing in nature. Thus, in constructing his table, he left a number of empty spaces to be filled in later by future discoveries. He gave to the "missing elements" names formed by adding the prefixes *eka* or *dvi*, meaning "first" and "second" in Sanskrit, to the names of neighboring homologous elements. In certain instances, he also reversed the atomic-weight order of elements in order to comply with the demands of the regular periodicity of their chemical properties. Using his table, shaky as it was, he was able to predict the physical and chemical properties of six "missing elements" on the basis of the known properties of their alleged neighbors. He called these elements eka-boron, eka-aluminum, eka-silicon, eka-manganese, dvi-manganese, and eka-tantalum. His predictions turned out to be in excellent agreement with the actually observed properties of the "missing elements" when they were finally found and named: scandium, gallium, germanium, technetium,* rhenium, and polo-

---

* Technetium, an unstable element normally non-existent in nature, was produced only recently in atomic piles.

nium. Just as an example, we give in Table 2 the comparison of Mendeleev's predictions of the properties of his hypothetical element "eka-silicon," with the actually observed properties of this element, which was found fifteen years later by a German chemist, Winkler, and given the name germanium.

TABLE 2

Mendeleev's prediction for eka-silicon (Es) (1871)	Winkler's data for germanium (Ge) (Discovered in 1886)
Atomic weight will be about 72	Atomic weight is 72.6
Will be obtained from EsO_2 or K_2EsF_6 by reduction with Na	Was obtained from K_2GeF_6 by reduction with Na
Will be a dark gray metal with high melting point and density about 5.5	Is a gray metal with melting point 958°C and density 5.36
On heating, Es will form the oxide EsO_2 with high melting point and density 4.7	Reacts with oxygen forming GeO_2 with melting point 1,100°C and density 4.7
The sulfide EsS_2 will be insoluble in water but soluble in ammonium sulfide	GeS_2 is insoluble in water but readily soluble in ammonium sulfide

Pretty good for a prediction at this stage in the development of chemistry!

By enumerating the elements from 1 (for hydrogen) and up as they come in the periodic system of elements, we obtain what is known as the *atomic numbers* of the elements. Thus, the atomic number of carbon is 6, that of mercury is 80, and that of mendelevium, 101. The atomic numbers of the six noble gases that form important landmarks of chemical periodicity are: 2, 10, 18, 36, 54, and 86. It is convenient to represent the periodic system of elements by a three-dimensional spiral structure that is shown in Fig. 2. The backbone of the structure is the column containing the noble gases running all the way from He down to Rn. The next column to the right contains the alkali metals, with hydrogen placed at the top because its chemical properties are similar to those of the alkali metals. To the left and around the corner from the noble gas column is the one containing the halogens. The first two periods, from He to F and from Ne to Cl, contain 8 elements each and fall neatly into

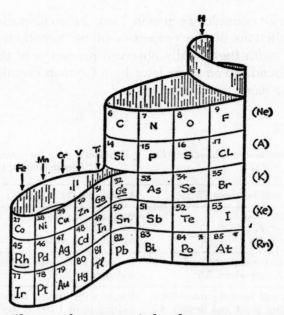

FIG. 2. *The periodic system of the elements represented as a wound ribbon. The diagram on the opposite page shows the other side of the second loop. At present the ribbon is cut at atomic number 101 (mendelevium). An asterisk indicates that the element is unstable (radioactive), and an asterisk in parenthesis indicates the presence of a radioactive isotope in the normally stable element. The properties of the underlined elements were predicted by Mendeleev.*

this scheme, but the next period contains 18 elements and constitutes a problem. On the basis of chemical properties, there seems to be no doubt that the 3 elements that follow A (K, Ca, and Sc) must be placed under the 3 corresponding elements (Na, Mg, and Al) of the previous period and that those preceding Kr (As, Se, and Br) should be under those preceding A (P, S, and Cl), but we do not seem to have places for the remaining 11 elements (Ti to Ge). To dispose of this difficulty, we place Ti and Ge, which both resemble Si, under that element and make an extra loop to accommodate the remaining 9 elements (V to Ga). The same situation arises in the next and in all of the following periods so that the extra loop perpetuates itself all the way to the end of the known sequence of elements. In the beginning of the fifth period we encounter further trouble of the same kind and are forced to build another extra loop to accommodate

10

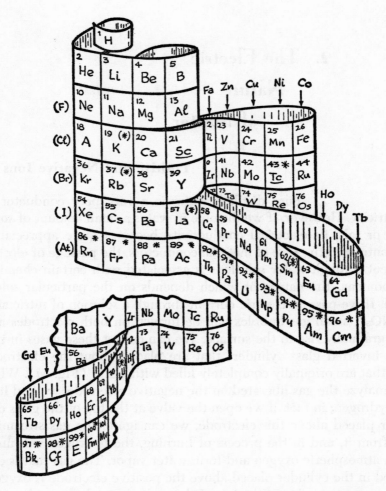

14 extra elements (Ce to Lu), known as the *rare earths*. The sixth and last period runs in the same way with most of the natural and artificial radioactive elements forming a loop under that formed by the rare earths.

Things become quite complicated, and Dmitri Ivanovich Mendeleev would probably be horrified by the looks of it, but that's how it is. Nevertheless, in spite of the complexity of the diagram (which reflects the complexity of the internal structure of the atom), the periodic system of elements in Fig. 2 gives a very good representation of the properties of the different elements.

2. The Electric Nature of Matter

Positive and Negative Ions

Pure distilled water is a very poor conductor of electricity. However, if we dissolve in water a small amount of some acid or salt, its electrical conductivity becomes quite appreciable. In contrast to the case of metallic conductors, the passage of electric current through water solutions is associated with certain chemical phenomena, the nature of which depends on the particular solute used. If we pass an electric current through a solution of nitric acid (HNO_3), small gas bubbles will be formed on both electrodes and will gradually rise to the surface. We can collect these gases in two long inverted glass cylinders that are placed about the electrodes and that are originally completely filled with water (Fig. 3a). When we analyze the gas liberated on the negative electrode, we find it to be hydrogen; in fact, if we open the valve at the top of the glass cylinder placed above this electrode, we can ignite the gas streaming out from it, and in the process of burning, the hydrogen will unite with atmospheric oxygen and form water vapor. The gas that is collected in the cylinder placed above the positive electrode is oxygen; if we open the valve at the top of that cylinder and place a burning match into the stream of outcoming gas, it will flare up more intensely because of the additional oxygen supply.

Thus, the passage of electric current decomposes water into its two elementary constituents, hydrogen and oxygen. How does this happen, and why should it require something dissolved in the water to get things going? The water molecule, H_2O, is quite tightly bound together and has very little tendency to break apart into ions. In fact, at room temperature only about 1 molecule in 10^7 will be split up into H^+ and OH^- ions. Such a small number of ions migrating

12

through an electric field constitutes so small a current that pure distilled water may be considered a fairly good insulator. However, the nitric acid molecules (as well as the molecules of salts and bases) split up readily into H^+ and NO_3^- when dissolved in water. Thus a large number of charged ions are provided, and their migration in the electric field between anode and cathode can constitute a large current.

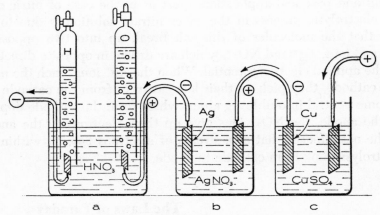

FIG. 3. *The electrolysis of water solutions of nitric acid (a), silver nitrate (b), and copper sulfate (c) by the same current.*

When an electric potential is applied to the cathode and anode, the positive ions of hydrogen are attracted to the negative electrode (cathode) and the negative NO_3^- ions are attracted to the positive electrode (anode). As the result of the ionic motion caused by these attractions, an electric current flows through the water solution, a current that would have been impossible in pure water. When the traveling ions H^+ and NO_3^- arrive at their respective electrodes, they release their electric charges into the metal; hydrogen rises to the surface in the form of tiny bubbles, while the neutral NO_3 reacts with water according to the equation $2NO_3 + H_2O \rightarrow 2HNO_3 + O$, liberating free oxygen and regenerating the original molecules of nitric acid. (There are secondary reactions producing oxides of nitrogen, but we may leave these complications to the chemists.) Thus, the passage of electric current through the water resulted in nothing more than the breaking up of the water molecules into their hydrogen and oxygen components.

If, instead of using nitric acid, we use one of its salts (in which hydrogen is replaced by a metal), the metal will be deposited on the surface of the negative electrode. When, for example, we pass an electric current through a solution of silver nitrate, $AgNO_3$ (Fig. 3b) we will notice that after a while the cathode will be covered with a thin layer of silver. This method of coating surfaces with thin layers of various metals is known as *electroplating* and has many useful and practical applications. Just as in the case of nitric acid, the electrolytic process in the silver nitrate solution is due to the fact that the molecules of this salt break up into two oppositely charged ions, Ag^+ and NO_3^-, which are driven in opposite directions by the applied electric potential. When the Ag^+ ions reach the negative cathode, they pick up their lost electrons from the cathode and become neutral insoluble Ag atoms which form the cathode deposit. At the anode, the NO_3^- ions give up their electrons to the anode, so the net effect is that of a stream of electrons flowing within the electrolysis tank from cathode to anode.

The Laws of Faraday

Michael Faraday, whose name is associated with the theory of electric and magnetic fields, was the first to investigate in detail the laws of electrolytic processes. He found first of all that, for each given salt solution, the amount of material deposited at the electrodes is directly proportional to the strength of the electric current and to its duration, or, in other words, that *the amount of material deposited on the electrodes is directly proportional to the total amount of electric charge which had passed through the solution.* From this first law of Faraday, we conclude that each ion of a given chemical substance carries a well-defined electric charge.

In further studies, Faraday investigated the relative amounts of electric charge carried by ions of different chemical substances. To compare these amounts, he passed an electric current consecutively through the solutions of several different substances, such as nitric acid, silver nitrate, and copper sulfate, as is shown in Fig. 3a, b, and c. In the case of nitric acid a certain amount of hydrogen gas was liberated on the cathode, while a certain amount of silver was deposited on the cathode in the case of the silver nitrate solution. Faraday measured the amounts of hydrogen and silver produced in these experiments and found that the ratio of the weight of deposited silver to the weight of liberated hydrogen was 107.02. Chemists had before this time determined from many ingenious experimental measurements the relative weights of the atoms of the chemical elements. These relative *atomic weights* were arranged in a table in which the weight of the oxygen atoms in the atmosphere was arbitrarily taken as 16.000, and the weights of all the other kinds of atom were expressed in units of $\frac{1}{16}$ of the weight of the oxygen atom; 107.02 is exactly the ratio of the atomic weight of silver to the atomic weight of hydrogen. Thus, Faraday concluded that the same number of atoms of Ag and H had been deposited and that *one ion of silver carries exactly the same electric charge as one ion of hydrogen.* It would be premature, however, to conclude that *all* ions carry the same electric charge. In fact, comparing the amount of silver liberated in the electrolysis of silver nitrate with that of copper liberated by the same electric current flowing for the same length of time in the electrolysis of copper sulfate, we find that the weight ratio of silver to copper is 3.40 instead of the 1.70 (107.9/63.5) that would correspond to one atom of silver per atom of copper. Notice, however, that 1.70 is exactly one-half of 3.40, and if we write the observed ratio in the form $(2 \times 107.9/63.5)$, we conclude that *one ion of copper carries twice as much electricity as one ion of silver.* We can interpret this by saying that the silver ion has lost one electron, while the copper ion has lost two electrons and therefore has a double positive charge. The number of electrons lost or gained by an ion is one aspect of what the chemist calls *valence.* Thus, hydrogen, silver, and the nitrate group (NO_3) have a valence of 1 (monovalent), copper and the sulfate group (SO_4) have a valence of 2 (divalent), whereas aluminum ions have a valence of 3 (trivalent).

Thus with several electrolytic cells in series, as in Fig. 3, for each atom of a monovalent element that is deposited, only $\frac{1}{2}$ of a divalent atom, or $\frac{1}{3}$ of a trivalent atom can be deposited. Chemists call the atomic weight divided by the valence the *equivalent weight,* and Faraday's second law of electrolysis states that *when the same amount of electric charge flows through different electrolytic cells, the amounts of the substances deposited (or liberated) are in direct proportion to their equivalent weights.*

For example, we can place two cells in series (which guarantees

that the same amount of charge will flow through each), one cell
containing silver nitrate and the other gold chloride (gold is trivalent), and allow current to flow until we have 1.00 gm of silver
deposited on the cathode of the first cell. At this time, how much
gold will have been deposited on the cathode of the other cell? The
equivalent weight of silver, since silver in monovalent, is the same
as its atomic weight, or 107.9. Gold has an equivalent weight of
$197.0/3 = 65.7$. Therefore, we can write:

$$\frac{\text{wt Ag deposited}}{\text{wt Au deposited}} = \frac{1.00}{x} = \frac{107.9}{65.7}$$

or: $x = 0.609$ gm Au deposited

It has been found that the passage of 96,500 coulombs of charge
will deposit a mass, in grams, of any element which is numerically
equal to its equivalent weight. (This amount of any element is more
formally called a *gram-equivalent weight;* one *gram-atomic weight*
is, of course, an amount of substance whose mass in grams equals
its atomic weight.)

The Passage of Electricity
through Gases

The next step in the study of the electric nature of matter was
made by J. J. Thomson (1856–1940), another famous Britisher
(Fig. 4). While Michael Faraday studied the passage of electric
current through liquids, J. J. (as he was known to his colleagues and
his students) later concentrated his attention on the electrical conductivity of gases.

When we walk in the evening along the downtown streets of a
modern city, we observe the bright display of neon (bright red) and
helium (pale green) advertising signs. Modern offices and homes
are illuminated by fluorescent light tubes. In all these cases, we
deal with the passage of high-voltage electric current through a
rarified gas—the phenomenon that was the object of the lifelong
studies of J. J. Thomson. As in the case of liquids, the current passing through a gas is due to the motion of positive and negative ions
driven in opposite directions by an applied electric field. The posi-

tive gas ions are similar to those encountered in the electrolysis of liquids (being the positively charged atoms or molecules of the substance in question), and the negative ions in this case are the much less massive singly charged particles that we now know to be electrons.

FIG. 4. *Sir J. J. Thomson (left), the discoverer of the electron, and Lord Rutherford, the discoverer of the nucleus, discuss some administrative problems in the courtyard of Cavendish Laboratory, Cambridge, England, 1929.*

To study these, at that time, mysterious particles Thomson, in 1897, used an instrument shown schematically in Fig. 5. It consisted of a glass tube containing highly rarified gas with a cathode placed at one end of it and an anode located in an extension on the side. Because of this arrangement, the negative ions, which form the "cathode-rays" that move from left to right in the drawing, miss the anode and fly into the right side of the tube. The tube broadens here, and its flat rear end is covered with a layer of fluorescent material which becomes luminous when bombarded by fast-moving

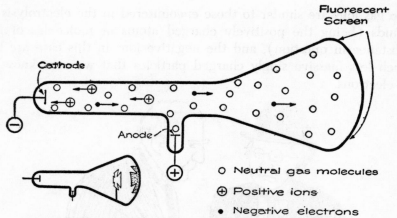

FIG. 5. *The passage of electric current through rarefied gas.*

particles. This tube is very similar to a modern TV tube where the image of pirouetting ballerinas or sweating prize fighters is also due to the fluorescence produced by a scanning electron beam. But in those pioneering days of what we now call *electronics,* one was satisfied with much simpler shows; placing a metal cross in the way of the beam, Thomson observed that it cast a shadow on the fluorescent screen, indicating that the particles in question were moving along straight lines, similar to light rays.

The Charge-to-Mass Ratio of an Electron

Thomson's next task was to study the deflection of the beam caused by electric and magnetic fields applied along its path. Indeed, since the beam was formed by a swarm of negatively charged particles, it should be deflected toward the positive pole of the condenser that produces the electric field shown in Fig. 6a. On the other hand, since a beam of charged particles is equivalent to an elecric current it should be deflected by a magnetic field directed perpendicularly to its track (Fig. 6b) according to the laws of electromagnetic interactions.

The deflection of a particle will depend, of course, on how much force is applied to it. For a charged particle in an electric field, the force depends only on the particle's charge and on the strength of the field. For a magnetic field, however, the situation is different; a magnetic field has no effect on a stationary charge but it does exert a force on an electric current, which is nothing more than a stream of *moving* charges. Hence the deflection in this case will depend on the strength of the magnetic field, the charge on the moving particle, and also on its velocity.

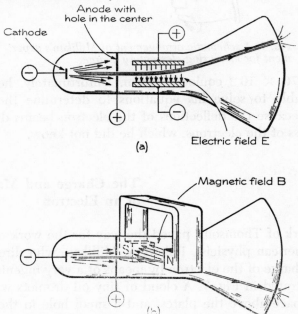

FIG. 6. *J. J. Thomson's method of measuring the velocity and the mass of electrons: (a) the electric deflection of an electron beam and (b) the magnetic deflection of such a beam.*

By combining the two experiments shown in Fig. 6a and b, Thomson was able was able to get valuable information about the little negatively charged particles called *electrons*. In a tube equipped with *both* an electric and a magnetic field, Thomson adjusted the strengths of the two fields so that the beam of electrons continued straight ahead without any deviation.

It can be shown from the theory of electric and magnetic deflections of a moving charge that the ratio e/m of the electron's charge to its mass can be obtained from the measured strengths of the fields. Thomson's experiments, and those of later workers, give the value

FIG. 7. *A schematic arrangement of Millikan's experiment for measuring elementary charge.*

$e/m = 1.76 \times 10^{-8}$ coulombs/gram. Unfortunately, however, he was not able to solve his equations to determine their electric charges, because the deflections of the electron beams depend also on the mass of the electrons, which he did not know.

The Charge and Mass of an Electron

This work of Thomson's paved the way for the work of the celebrated American physicist, Robert A. Millikan, who directly measured the charge of the electron by means of a very ingenious experiment illustrated in Fig. 7. A cloud of tiny oil droplets was sprayed into the space above the plates, and a small hole in the top plate was uncovered long enough for one of the droplets to drift down through the hole into the space between the plates, where it could be observed through a microscope set into the wall of the vessel. By means of a relationship known as *Stokes' law*, the weight of a small droplet can be determined from the rate at which it settles downward through the air. Millikan could measure the rate of settling with no electric field between the plates and thus compute the weight of the droplet.

Ultraviolet light can pull electrons away from the molecules of objects on which it falls, so by allowing a beam of utraviolet light to shine between the plates, Millikan could cause the droplet to have a slight charge that could change suddenly from time to time as it collided with charged air molecules. By varying the potential applied across his plates, he could adjust the electric field until the droplet would hang motionless, neither rising nor falling. Under these equilibrium conditions, the upward force caused by the electric field was just equal to the weight of the droplet, and thus:

$$Eq = mg$$

from which q, the charge on the droplet, could be easily figured.

It turned out that all the charges measured in this way were small integral multiples of a certain quantity that was apparently the elementary electric charge, or the charge of an electron. Numerically he found that the value of this elementary charge is 1.60×10^{-19} coulomb, or 4.80×10^{-10} esu.

From Thomson's charge-to-mass ratio and a direct knowledge of the charge on an electron, the mass of an electron can be computed to be:

$$\frac{1.60 \times 10^{-19} \text{ coulombs}}{1.76 \times 10^{8} \text{ coulombs/gram}} = 9.11 \times 10^{-28} \text{ grams}$$

The discovery of the electron as representing a free electric charge and the possibility of its extraction from neutral atoms was the first indication that *atoms are not indivisible particles but complex mechanical systems composed of positively and negatively charged parts*. Positive ions were interpreted as having a *deficiency* of one or more electrons, whereas negative ions were considered as atoms having an *excess* of electrons.

Canal Rays and Isotopes

While the study of cathode rays in Thomson's tube led to the discovery of electrons, *canal rays*, which are a stream of positively charged gas ions, were also very helpful for the understanding of the inner nature of the atom. The apparatus Thomson used for the study of canal rays was a modification of the tube used for determining the e/m ratio, and is shown in Fig. 8. A small amount of gas is left within the tube, and when a swiftly moving electron collides with a gas molecule, an electron is likely to be knocked off, making the molecule into an ion with a positive charge. The mass and electric charge of these positively charged canal rays can be analyzed by deflecting them in electric and magnetic fields. Thomson used parallel electric and magnetic fields, so that passing ions received thrusts in both vertical and horizontal directions. Although we will not stop to do it, it is not difficult to show that a stream of positive ions, all of the same charge and mass, will leave a trace in the shape of a parabola on the fluorescent end of the tube. Those ions having high speeds will be deviated little; slower ions will strike farther out on the parabola. The mass of the ions can be computed quite accurately from the geometry of the parabola.

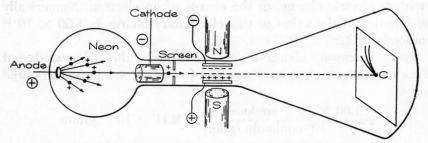

FIG. 8. *The apparatus that led to the discovery of isotopes. Positive ions of neon were accelerated by an electric field and formed a thin beam after passing through a slit in a screen. The beam was deflected by a combined electric and magnetic field and fell on the fluorescent screen at the far right end of the tube. If all Ne ions had the same mass, though different velocities, the line on the screen would be in the shape of a parabola. But there were three different parabolas corresponding to the masses 20, 21, and 22.*

In measuring the mass of the particles forming canal rays in a tube filled with neon gas, Thomson expected to confirm the chemical value of the atomic weight of neon, which was known to be 20.183. However, instead of this value he got only 20.0, which was considerably lower and well beyond the limits of possible experimental error. The discrepancy was explained when Thomson noticed that the beam of neon ions passing through the magnetic and electric fields was not deflected as a single beam, but was split into three branches (Fig. 8).* The particles in the main branch, containing over 90.5 per cent of all the neon ions, had a mass value of 20.0; the other fainter branch contained 9.2 per cent, and had a mass of 22.0, and a still fainter branch containing 0.3 per cent of mass 21.

This was very remarkable! Here Thomson had found two kinds

* Thomson's co-worker, F. W. Aston, later used more complex, improved equipment, and found a very faint third branch, which is also shown in the drawing.

of neon atoms, *identical in chemical nature and in their optical spectra, but different in mass.* On top of this, both mass values were almost exactly integral numbers. Ordinary neon, then, was actually a mixture of two different neons (three, in fact, as was discovered later) and the chemical weight was just the average weight of this mixture.

The different types of neon were called *isotopes* of this element, which means in Greek "same place" and refers to the fact that all the neons of different weight occupy the same place in the table of the elements. We usually denote isotopes by placing an index indicating the mass at the upper right corner of the symbol of the element; thus Ne^{20}, Ne^{21}, and Ne^{22} stand for the three neon isotopes, while Ne refers to their natural mixture.

Thomson's original crude apparatus has been improved by Aston, A. J. Dempster, and K. T. Bainbridge, and the modern *mass spectrograph,* as these instruments are called, can determine the relative masses of isotopes with great accuracy.

Further studies have shown that practically every element represents a mixture of several isotopes. While in some cases (as in gold and iodine) one isotope accounts for 100 per cent of the material, in many other cases (as in chlorine and zinc), different isotopes have comparable abundances. The isotopic composition of some of the chemical elements is shown in Table 3.

TABLE 3

Atomic Number	Name	Isotopic composition with percentage shown in parentheses
1	Hydrogen	1(99.985); 2(0.015)
6	Carbon	12(98.9); 13(1.1)
7	Nitrogen	14(99.64); 15(0.36)
8	Oxygen	16(99.76); 17(0.04); 18(0.20)
17	Chlorine	35(75.4); 37(24.6)
30	Zinc	64(48.89); 66(27.81); 67(4.07); 68(18.61); 70(0.62)
48	Cadmium	106(1.215); 108(0.875), 110(12.39); 111(12.75); 112(24.07); 113(12.26); 114(28.86); 116(7.58)
80	Mercury	196(0.15); 198(10.02); 199(16.84); 200(23.13); 201(13.21); 202(28.80); 204(6.85)

The remarkable fact that we notice from this table is that *whereas the atomic weight of chemical elements is not necessarily an integral number, the weight of individual isotopes is always very close to an integer.* This fact bolstered an important hypothesis that was first proposed a century ago by the British chemist, William Prout, who considered all elements to be some kind of condensation of a single primary element: hydrogen. Prout's hypothesis, proposed very early in the development of scientific chemistry and based on the assumption of the unity of matter borrowed from medieval alchemy, was rejected by his contemporaries, who argued that the atomic weights of chlorine and mercury are far from being integral. Only after Aston's discovery of isotopes was Prout's idea reinstated in its own right, and it became, in a somewhat modified form, one of the cornerstones of the modern theory of the internal structure of matter.

Thomson's Atomic Model

On the basis of his experiments, J. J. Thompson proposed a model of internal atomic structure (Fig. 9) according to which atoms consisted of a positively charged substance (positive electric fluid) distributed uniformly over the entire body of the atom, with negative electrons imbedded in this continuous positive charge like seeds in a watermelon. Since electrons repel each other but are, on the other hand, attracted to the center of the positive charge, they were supposed to assume certain stable positions inside the body of the atom. If this distribution were disturbed by some external force, such as, for example, a violent collision between two atoms in a hot gas, the electrons were supposed to start vibrating around their equilibrium positions, emitting light waves of corresponding frequencies.

Many calculations were made in an attempt to correlate the emission frequencies of electrons in Thomson's atom with the actually observed frequencies of light emitted by different elements, but there was no success. After a number of futile efforts, it became rather clear that although Thomson's model considered an atom to be a complex system formed by positive and negative electric

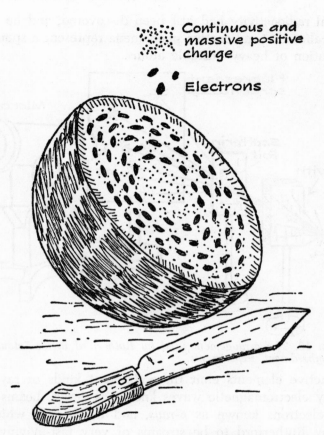

Continuous and massive positive charge

Electrons

FIG. 9. *J. J. Thomson's "watermelon" model of an atom.*

charges rather than an elementary indivisible body and represented a considerable progress toward the truth, it was not yet the truth itself.

Rutherford's Atomic Model

The honor of giving the first correct description of the distribution of positive and negative charges within the atom belongs to a New Zealand-born physicist, Ernest Rutherford (1871–1937), who was later elevated to the rank of Lord Rutherford for his important scientific achievements. Young Rutherford entered physics during that crucial period of its development when the phenomenon of natural radioactivity had just been discovered, and he was the first to realize that radioactive phenomena represent a spontaneous disintegration of heavy unstable atoms.

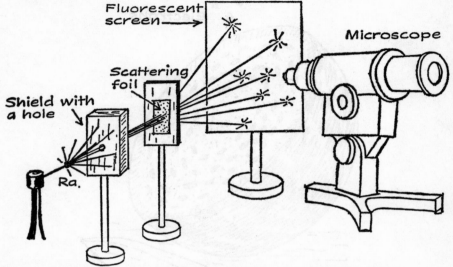

FIG. 10. *The arrangement used by Rutherford in his "atomic bombardment" experiments.*

Radioactive elements emit three different kinds of rays: high-frequency electromagnetic waves known as *γ-rays*, beams of fast-moving electrons known as *β-rays*, and the *α-rays*, which were shown by Rutherford to be streams of very fast-moving helium ions. Rutherford realized that very important information about the inner structure of atoms can be obtained by the study of violent collisions between onrushing α-particles and the atoms of various materials forming the target. This started him on a series of epoch-making atomic bombardment experiments that revealed the true nature of the atom and led ultimately to the present atomic energy developments. The experimental arrangement used by Rutherford in his studies was exceedingly simple (Fig. 10): a speck of α-emitting radioactive material at *A*, a lead diaphragm, *B*, that cuts out a thin beam of α-rays, the material under investigation in the form of a piece of thin foil, *C*, a fluorescent screen, *D*, and a microscope, *E*, to observe the tiny flashes of light, or scintillations, originating when an α-particle hits the screen. Before the material to be studied was inserted between the diaphragm and the fluorescent screen, scintillations were observed only in a small, sharply defined area immediately opposite the opening of the diaphragm. The introduction of the foil into the path of the α-rays, however, caused a considerable scattering of the original beam with many of the α-particles being deflected by quite large angles, and some of them even being thrown almost directly backward. Counting, through a microscope, the number of scintillations observed in different directions with respect to the original beam, Rutherford was able to construct a curve giving the relative scattering intensity as a function of the angle. One of these curves, pertaining to the scattering of radium α-particles in aluminum, is shown in Fig. 11.

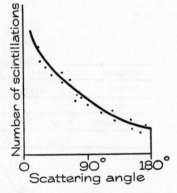

FIG. 11. *The number of scattered α-particles depends on the angle of scattering in the case of α-rays in aluminum.*

Comparing the results of these experiments with the scattering that was theoretically expected on the basis of J. J. Thomson's atomic model, Rutherford noticed at once that something was drastically wrong. In fact, if the positive charge, and most of the atomic mass associated with it, were uniformly distributed through the entire volume of the atom, the collisions between the α-particles of the beam and the atoms of the target could not possibly deflect the incident particles by more than just a few degrees. In order to produce a sufficiently strong electrostatic repulsion between the positive charge of the bombarded atom and the positive charge of the incident α-particle, *all positive charges, along with most of the atomic mass, had to be concentrated in a very small central region of the colliding particles,* a region which Rutherford named the *atomic nucleus* (Fig. 12). But, if all the positive charge of an atom is concentrated in its very center, the main body of the atom must be formed by nothing more than a swarm of negatively charged electrons moving freely through space. In order not to fall into the central nucleus under the action of the forces of electrostatic attraction, the elecrons must be rotating very rapidly around the center of the system. Thus, in one bold stroke Rutherford transformed the static "watermelon model" of J. J. Thomson into a dynamic "planetary model" in which the nucleus plays the role of the sun and the electrons correspond to the individual planets of the solar system.

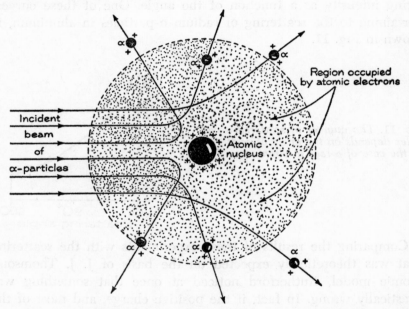

FIG. 12. *The deflection of α-particles due to the positive charge of the atomic nucleus.*

The strong concentration of atomic mass and positive charge in the very center of the atom not only made possible the explanation of the large scattering angles observed by Rutherford in his experiments but also led to a simple quantitative expression for the number of α-particles scattered in different directions. Since the electrons forming the outer body of the atom are very much lighter than the central nucleus and are also much lighter than the alpha particle being deflected, the role of the electrons in a collision between an atom and an alpha particle can be completely disregarded. The scattering problem is thus reduced to a collision between two mass points that repel each other with a force inversely proportional to the square of the distance. In the case of attractive forces, such as we have when planets rotate around the sun and electrons rotate around an atomic nucleus, the inverse square law of interaction leads to elliptical motion, but repulsive inverse square forces lead to hyperbolic trajectories. A comparatively simple mathematical calculation (which is, nevertheless, too complicated to reproduce here) leads to the conclusion that the number of incident particles that are scattered at a certain angle θ must be inversely proportional to the fourth power of the sine of $\frac{1}{2}\theta$, a conclusion which stood in perfect agreement with the results of Rutherford's original experiments shown in Fig. 11.

Conduction of Electricity in Solids

We have discussed the passage of an electric current through liquid solutions of acids and salts and through rarefied gases. In the first case, the current was due to the motion of positively and negatively charged ions, such as Ag^+ and NO_3^-, shouldering their way through the crowd of water molecules. In the second case, we dealt with positively charged ions flying in one direction and free negative charges, or electrons, flying in the opposite direction. But what happens when an electric current passes through solids, and why are some solids (all of them classed as metals) rather good conductors of electricity while the rest of them, known as *insulators*, hardly pass any electric current at all? Since in solid materials all atoms and molecules are rigidly held in fixed positions and cannot move freely as they do in gaseous or liquid materials, the passage of electricity through solids cannot be due to the motion of charged atoms or atomic groups. Thus, the only active electric carrier can be an electron, which, being much smaller than the atoms and molecules forming the crystalline lattice of a solid, should be able to pass between big atoms as easily as a small speedboat can pass through a heavily crowded anchorage of bulky merchantmen. Indeed, this is exactly what takes place in metallic conductors. The high electrical conductivity of these substances is inseparably connected with the presence of a large number of free mobile electrons that rush to and fro through the rigid crystalline lattices (Fig. 13). In metals the atoms are packed considerably tighter than in other substances, and this, among other things, accounts for the relatively high density of metals. As the result of such close packing and squeezing of metallic atoms, some of their structural electrons (about one electron per atom) get detached from the main atomic body and travel at random through the metallic crystal lattice.

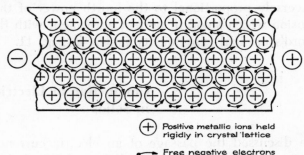

      (+) Positive metallic ions held
            rigidly in crystal lattice

      → Free negative electrons

FIG. 13. *The motion of free electrons explains the passage of electric current through metals.*

In the case of non-metals, such as sulfur, each atom holds tightly all of its 16 electrons, and the application of an electric field can cause nothing more than a slight deformation (electric polarization) of the atoms forming the crystal lattice. On the other hand, in the case of aluminum only 12 out of its 13 electrons are retained in each atom while the thirteenth "black sheep" electron is detached from the basic structure and is free to move wherever the applied electric potential urges it to go.

Electrical Conductivity vs. Heat Conductivity

In considering the electrical conductivity of different metals we find a significant parallelism between electrical and heat conductivities; electrical conductivities of different metals are directly proportional to their heat conductivities. This fact clearly indicates that the two phenomena are closely related to each other, and, indeed, the electron theory of metals ascribes their heat conduction to the *diffusion of free electrons* from the heated end of a metallic object to the cooler end. Since the electrons in a metal can move between the atoms forming its lattice with the greatest of ease, the increased thermal agitation existing at the heated end of a metallic object spreads out very quickly toward its cooler end, in contrast to the case of insulators where all electrons are bound to their atoms and thermal agitation propagates through the material only via the interactions between neighboring vibrating molecules.

The electron theory of metals leads to a rather simple mathematical formula for the coefficients of electrical and thermal conductivities. The formula expresses these coefficients through the mass and charge of electrons, their velocity within the metal, and the distance they travel between two collisions with the atoms forming the lattice (the so-called mean free path). It turns out first of all that, for a given temperature, the coefficients of both electrical and thermal conductivities must be proportional to the number of free electrons in the metal in question, from which it follows that *the ratio of thermal and electrical conductivities must be the same for different metals at a given temperature.* Theoretical studies of the motion of free electrons through metals lead further to the conclusion that *the ratio of thermal and electrical conductivities must increase in direct proportion to the absolute temperature of the conductor.*

This statement concerning the relation between the thermal and electrical conductivities of metals constitutes the so-called Wiedeman-Franz law, which was found empirically long before the electron theory of metals was formulated. Table 4 shows how well this law holds for different metals at widely different temperatures.

The expected numerical value of this ratio calculated from the electron theory of metals turns out to be 2.7×10^{-13}, in good agreement with the empirical values listed in the table. The agreement between the observed and the theoretically predicted correlation between the thermal and electrical conductivities of metals and the absolute temperature is a typical example of how theoretical as-

TABLE 4

THE RATIOS OF THERMAL AND ELECTRICAL CONDUCTIVITIES FOR DIFFERENT METALS DIVIDED BY THE CORRESPONDING ABSOLUTE TEMPERATURES

(All numbers given in the table have to be multiplied by 10^{-13})

Temp	Copper	Lead	Silver	Tin	Zinc
−100°C (173°abs.)	2.39	2.61	2.52	2.76	2.63
0°C (273°abs.)	2.53	2.78	2.56	2.74	2.70
100°C (373°abs.)	2.55	2.76	2.61	2.74	2.56

sumptions about the internal structure of matter increase our understanding of empirically established relations between several, at first sight, unrelated phenomena.

Thermo-ionic Emission

As we have seen, the principle of modern electronic tubes is based on the fact that red-hot metallic surfaces emit large numbers of free electrons. This phenomenon (first investigated by the British physicist, Richardson, and sometimes called the *Richardson Effect*) is easily explained by the electron theory of metals and is, in a way, similar to the evaporation of liquids. Just as in the case of liquids, where the molecules are normally prevented from crossing the surface by mutual cohesive forces (surface tension forces), free electrons are held inside the metal by electric attraction to the positive ions forming the lattice. But, at sufficiently high temperatures, the kinetic energy of a small fraction of free electrons inside the metal becomes sufficiently high to overcome this surface barrier, and these electrons fly freely into space, to the great delight of physicists and radio engineers. The temperature at which the "evaporation" of electrons begins to be perceptible depends on the strength of the electric forces holding them in and is different for different metals. As in liquids, where the evaporation process goes easily in ether and alcohol, less easily in water, and quite slowly in heavy oils, we observe different rates of electron evaporation from different metals (fast for cesium, slower for tungsten, and quite slowly for platinum).

Semiconductors

Some materials cannot be classified as either insulators or good conductors; thermal agitation of the atoms can knock loose a few electrons and permit the material to be slightly conductive. Such materials are known as *semiconductors*. A small amount of the proper kind of impurity in the crystalline structure of a semiconductor may, however, make it enormously more conductive. The three pictures in Fig. 14 explain how and why the presence of foreign atoms in the originally completely regular lattice may lead to such a large increase of electrical conductivity.

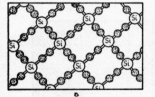 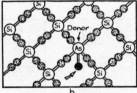 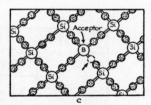

FIG. 14. *The impurities in the crystalline structure of a semiconductor make the semiconductor very conductive.*

In Fig. 14*a* we see a pure silicon crystal in which each atom of silicon, having a chemical valence 4, is connected with four of its neighbors by four bonds. Diagram 14*b* shows the situation that arises when one atom of silicon is replaced by an atom of arsenic, which has a valence of 5. The four valence electrons of the As atom form connections (bonds) with the four neighboring Si atoms, while the fifth "black sheep" electron is left unemployed and free to travel from place to place. The impurity atoms that give rise to free electrons in this way are known as *donors*. A reverse situation occurs when the Si atom is replaced by a trivalent atom of boron (*c*). In this case there will be a vacant place, or an *electron hole*, that breaks up the spotless regularity of the silicon crystal lattice. The impurity atoms that give rise to such "holes" are known as *acceptors*. A hole formed near a foreign atom present in the lattice may be filled up by an electron originally belonging to one of the neighboring silicon atoms, but in filling this hole the electron will leave a hole at the place where it was originally located. If this hole is filled by another neighboring electron, a new hole will move one step farther out (Fig. 15). Thus, we can visualize the hole of

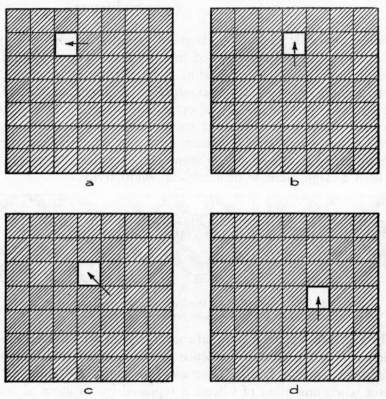

FIG. 15. *The successive fillings of a "hole" by neighboring electrons (represented by shaded squares) make the "hole" move to the right and downwards.*

that type as an "object" that is moving through the crystal, carrying a deficiency of negative charge, or, what is the same, a positive electric charge. Semiconductors that contain donor atoms and free electrons are known as *n-type* semiconductors; those with acceptor atoms and holes are called *p-type* semiconductors (*n* and *p* stand for a negative and positive charge of electric carriers). The electrical conductivity of n-type semiconductors is determined by the number of free electrons per unit valence and the ease with which they move through the crystal lattice, while in the case of p-type semiconductors it depends on the number and mobility of the holes.

Crystal Rectifiers

Suppose now that we put into contact two crystals: an n-type crystal containing free electrons and a p-type crystal containing electron holes (Fig. 16). Some of the electrons from the n-region

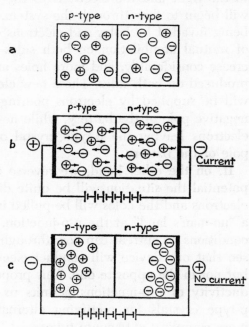

FIG. 16. *The motion of electrons and holes across a p-n-junction. (a) In the absence of an electric field, some electrons get into the p-type crystal and some holes into the n-type crystal. (b) If the field is directed from the p-type to the n-type crystal, a continuous electric current will flow through the junction. (c) If the direction of the field is reversed no current will flow.*

will diffuse into the p-region, while some holes from the p-region will diffuse into the n-region. Thus the n-type crystal will become slightly positively charged whereas the p-type crystal will carry an equal negative charge. Between these opposite charges on both sides of the interface (known as an *n-p-junction*) there will be an electric force of attraction which will prevent further diffusion, and the situation will be stabilized with a certain number of holes in the n-type crystal and an equal number of electrons in the p-type crystal. It must be remembered, however, that when free electrons and electron holes exist side by side in a given material, they can be mutually "annihilated" by a free electron filling a hole. In order to compensate for the losses due to this annihilation process, a small number of electrons and holes will continue to diffuse in opposite directions through the n-p-junction.

Let use see what happens now if we apply an electric potential at the two ends of our crystal pair. If the positive pole of a battery is connected to the p-type crystal and the negative pole to the n-type crystal (Fig. 16b), there will be a force driving the holes to the right and the electrons to the left, and an electric current will begin to flow through the system. Since both crystals are now being invaded by holes and electrons crossing the border, the rate of mutual annihilation on both sides of the n-p-junction will increase considerably, and more holes and electrons will have to be produced on both sides. These new electrons for the n-type crystal will be supplied by electrons pouring through the wire from the negative pole of the battery, while new holes will be produced by electrons leaving the p-type crystal on their way to the positive pole of the battery.

If, on the other hand, we reverse the direction of the electric potential the situation will be quite different (Fig. 16c). Now the electrons and the holes will be pulled in opposite directions, leaving a "no-man's land" at the n-p-junction. It is clear that under these conditions no current can flow through our double crystal. Thus we see that our device will conduct electric current in one direction but not in the opposite one. This property of one-way electric conductivity of n-p-junctions permits us to use pairs of n-type and p-type crystals for rectifying alternating current instead of the more complicated vacuum tubes.

Transistors

A thin layer of a p-type crystal sandwiched between two n-type crystals can be made to function in the same manner as a vacuum tube, and is called a *transistor*. The principal advantage of transistors over vacuum tubes lies in the fact that the controlled flow of electrons takes place entirely *within solid material.* Thus it is not necessary to use a large amount of power to keep a filament red hot to "boil" electrons off into space. This, in addition to their simplicity, sturdiness, and small size, is rapidly causing transistors to take the place of vacuum tubes in many fields of electronics.

Solar and Radioactive Batteries

The properties of the n-p-junction between two crystals can also be used for the direct transformation into electric energy of both solar radiation and the rays emitted by radioactive materials. When radiation is absorbed in the material of a semiconducting crystal, it knocks off some electrons from the atoms to which they belong, thus increasing the number of free electrons and electron holes. This increased number of electric carriers disturbs the electrostatic balance at the interface between the n- and p-type crystals and causes an electric current to run from the crystal containing acceptors to the crystal containing donors. A workable solar battery of this kind was recently developed in the laboratories of the Bell Telephone Company. It consists of a silicon crystal with a slight arsenical contamination (donor) through its entire body, except for a thin upper p-type layer (one ten-thousandth of an inch thick), which is contaminated by boron and serves as an acceptor. The sun's rays that fall on the upper surface of this device are absorbed in the material of the crystal, produce extra electrons and extra electron holes, and stimulate an electron potential of about one-half volt. This device has about a 20 per cent efficiency, as compared with only a few per cent efficiency of all previously proposed devices, and it produces a power of about 0.01 watt per cm^2 of its surface. A battery with a working surface of 10 sq m (about 100 sq ft) installed on the roof of a house will produce a power of 100 watts, which, when stored in ordinary electric storage batteries, is sufficient to operate a 100-watt electric bulb at night for the same number of hours that the sun was shining during the day. Because of the present high cost of producing the elements of a solar battery, it would be highly irrational to use it for the purpose of saving on the electric bill, but such batteries will undoubtedly find many useful applications, one of which has been the production of power for running the electrical equipment in experimental satellites.

The principle of the solar battery can be used also for the direct transformation of α-, β-, and γ-rays emitted by radioactive materials, such as fission products, into the energy of electric current. If such a device can be constructed with an efficiency comparable to that of the solar battery, the fission products that result from the operation of plutonium-producing piles and various nuclear power reactors could be used to run small household gadgets and devices employed in many other walks of life.

3. The Quantum
of Radiant
Energy

The Ultraviolet Catastrophe

The radiation emitted by heated bodies represents a mixture of all different wave lengths. An increase in temperature ($T_{abs.}$) results in a rapid increase in the total amount of emitted radiant energy (proportional to $T_{abs.}^4$) and in the shortening of the prevailing wave length (proportional to $T_{abs.}^{-1}$). Comparing the curves showing the distribution of energy at different wave lengths of radiation for various temperatures with the curves showing the distribution of energy (or velocities) in the molecules of a gas, we cannot help noticing a certain analogy between them: in both cases, the curves show a well-defined maximum which shifts its position with the change of temperature.

During the last decade of the nineteenth century, a British physicist and astronomer, Sir James Jeans (1877–1946), made an attempt to treat the problem of the distribution of energy between different wave lengths of radiant energy in the same statistical way as Maxwell had done in the case of the distribution of energy between different molecules of a gas. To do this, Jeans considered radiant energy of different wave lengths enclosed in a cube, the walls of which are made of ideal mirrors reflecting a full 100 per cent of any radiation falling on them. Of course, this so-called Jeans's cube is just an abstraction (since there are no such mirrors) and can be used only for the purpose of purely theoretical arguments; but in physics, we very often use idealized models of this sort.

In Fig. 17, we give a schematic picture of Jeans's cube and various waves that can exist within it. The situation is similar to that of the sound waves that can exist inside a cubical enclosure with perfectly reflecting walls, or to that of standing waves of any kind. The reflecting walls must be nodes of the standing waves, so that *l*, the distance between the walls of the cube, is an integral number of half wave lengths.

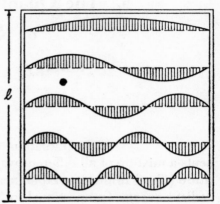

FIG. 17. *A cross section of "Jeans's cube," showing the different waves that can exist inside it. Only the waves propagating in a horizontal direction are shown here. The black dot is a tiny coal dust particle.*

l

The longest wave has a wave length twice the length of the side *l* of the cube, and the next possible wave lengths are: 1, ⅔, ½, ⅖, etc., of *l*. We also assume that the box contains one or more "coal dust particles" that are introduced here to permit the exchange of energy between the different modes of vibrations existing in the box. (These particles are supposed to absorb the energy from the vibrations of one wave length and to re-emit it at a different wave length.)

We can now draw an analogy between the different vibrations within the Jeans's cube and the molecules of gas contained in a similar cubical enclosure. Just as in the case of the gas where the total available kinetic energy can be distributed in various ways between individual molecules, the total available radiant energy within Jeans's cube can be distributed in various ways between the vibrations of different wave lengths. The law of equipartition of energy states that *all the molecules of gas share equally in the distribution of the total available energy,* so that the mean energy of each molecule is simply equal to the total amount of energy divided by the number of molecules in the box. The same kind of statistical considerations led to the conclusion that the total radiant energy in the Jeans's cube should be equally distributed between the vibrations of all different wave lengths. But here came a very serious difficulty! Whereas the number of molecules forming a gas, though very large, is still finite, *the number of possible vibrations in Jeans's box is infinite,* since we can continue beyond any limit the sequence of possible wave lengths given above. Thus, if the equipartition law holds in this case, as it certainly should, each individual vibration would get an infinitely small share of the total energy. Since, on the other hand, the sequence of wave lengths continues indefinitely in the direction of shorter and shorter wave lengths, *all the available energy will be concentrated in the region of infinitely short waves.* Thus, if we fill Jeans's cube with red light, it should rapidly become violet, ultraviolet, then turn into X-rays, into gamma rays (such as are emitted by radioactive substances), and so on beyond any limit. What happens to radiant energy in the idealized case of Jeans's cube must also hold for the radiation in all practical cases, and the light emitted by red-hot pieces of coal in the fireplace should be turned into deadly gamma rays even before it leaves the grate! Or, at least, that is what would happen if the laws of classical physics were applicable to radiant energy. This "Jeans's paradox," also known as the "ultraviolet catastrophe," gave a terrible blow to the self-satisfied classical physics of the nineteenth century and catapulted it into an entirely new field of thought and experience—now known as *quantum theory*—unprecedented in the history of physics. Although the advanced mathematics needed for detailed quantitative study of the quantum theory is not easy, the underlying concepts are not too difficult, even without extensive mathematics; and before finishing this chapter, the reader should acquire a general idea of what it is all about.

The Birth of the Energy Quantum

Just before the close of the last century, in Christmas week, 1899, at a meeting of the German Physical Society in Berlin the German physicist, Max Planck (1858–1947), presented his views on how to save the world from the perils of Jeans's ultraviolet catastrophe. His proposal was as paradoxical as Jeans's paradox itself, but it certainly was helpful. In a way, Planck's proposal can be considered as the extension of Democritus' hypothesis concerning the atomic structure of matter to the problem of radiant energy. Following

Democritus, who insisted that matter cannot be subdivided into arbitrarily small portions and that one atom is the smallest possible amount of matter, Max Planck assumed that *there must exist a smallest portion of energy*, and he gave these smallest portions of energy the name *energy quanta*. According to this revolutionary view, the bright days of the sun that pour through the windows or the soft light that radiates from a table lamp *do not represent a continuous flow of light waves, but rather a stream of individual "energy packages" or "light quanta"* (Fig. 18). To each kind of ra-

FIG. 18. *The old and the new picture of sunlight coming through the window: (a) old view of light beam as formed by continuous wave trains,* the amplitude *of which increases with the intensity of light; (b) new view of light beam as formed by individual vibrating "light quanta,"* the number *of which determines the intensity of light.*

diation corresponds a definite amount of energy which can be carried in one package, and it is just as nonsensical to talk about three-quarters of a quantum of green light as it is to talk about three-quarters of an atom of copper. Planck assumed that the light quanta of different types of radiation carry different amounts of energy and that *the amount of energy of a light quantum is inversely proportional to the wave length of the radiation, or (what is the same) directly proportional to its frequency.* Writing v (vibrations/second) for the frequency of the radiation and E for the energy of the light quantum, we can express Planck's assumption in the form:

$$E = h \times v$$

where h is the coefficient of proportionality known as *Planck's constant* or the *quantum constant*.

How does Planck's assumption of light quanta help to remove the perils of Jeans's ultraviolet catastrophe? To understand this, let us look further into the consequences of the basic assumption that $E = h\nu$, that is, that radiant energy, such as light, flies about in packets of energy, the sizes of which are proportional to the frequency of the radiation. The long wave-length waves of radio have low frequencies (recall that frequency equals velocity divided by wave length; $\nu = v/\lambda$; and that $v = c$ for all electromagnetic radiation); hence their quanta of energy are small. Visible light, with frequencies a billion times greater, comes in quanta whose energy is also a billion times greater. Energy must be absorbed and emitted in whole quanta, exactly—no fractional parts of quanta are allowed.

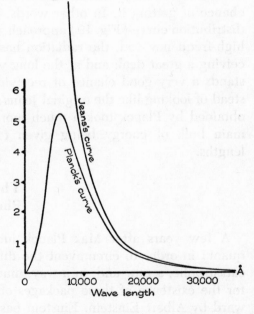

FIG. 19. *Jeans's curve and Planck's curve representing the dependence of energy on the wave length.*

The difference in the size of the demands between long-wave (low-frequency) and short-wave (high-frequency) radiation has an important effect on the application of the equipartition principle. If, for example, $6.00 must be distributed among six persons, none of whom presents any minimum demand, the fairest distribution would be to give $1.00 to each of them. Suppose, however, that Mr. A would take no less than $1.00, Mr. B no less than $2.00, and so on, up to Mr. F, who would accept no less than $6.00. It would certainly be unfair to give all six dollars to Mr. F and deprive everyone else of any share. It would not be fair either to give $5.00 to Mr. E (his minimum demand) and the remaining $1.00 to Mr. A. Clearly, the most reasonable distribution of the total money available would be to give $1.00 to Mr. A, $2.00 to Mr. B, $3.00 to Mr. C, and to deprive the Messrs. D, E, and F of any share because of their unreasonably high demands.

Planck did something very like this in the problem of distributing the total energy among vibrations of different frequencies existing within an enclosure of given size. His solution can be considered to take the form of a probability distribution—the vibrations with high demands have a very small chance of having their demands satisfied. Low-frequency radiation, which asks but little, has a very good chance of getting it. In other words, both ends of Planck's energy distribution curve (Fig. 19) approach zero; at the short wave-length, high-frequency end, the radiation has practically no chance of receiving a great deal; and at the long wave-length end the radiation stands a very good chance of receiving practically nothing. So instead of looking like the original Jeans's curve the distribution curve obtained by Planck took a much more reasonable shape, with the main bulk of energy being given to certain intermediate wave lengths.

The Puzzle of the Photoelectric Effect

A few years after Max Planck introduced the notion of light quanta in order to circumvent the difficulties of Jeans's ultraviolet catastrophe, a new and, in a way, much more persuasive argument for the existence of these packages of radiant energy was put forward by Albert Einstein. Einstein based his argument on the laws of the *photo-electric effect*, i.e., the ability of various materials to emit free electrons when irradiated by visible or ultraviolet light. An elementary arrangement for the demonstration of the photoelectric effect is shown in Fig. 20. A freshly sandpapered piece of zinc, *P*, is attached to an electroscope and given a *negative* charge. If light from an electric arc is allowed to fall directly on the zinc plate, the electroscope leaves will come together, showing that the plate has lost its charge. The closer the arc light is to the plate, the more rapidly will the charge be lost; conversely, as the experiment is repeated with the arc removed to greater and greater distances, the charge will be lost more slowly. However, we find that if a sheet of ordinary glass is put between the arc light and the zinc, the zinc will retain its negative charge, even if the arc is brought very close. Also, we find that if the zinc is originally given a *positive* charge, the arc light will have little apparent effect on the rate at which the charge is lost.

FIG. 20. *When struck by ultraviolet radiation from an arc light, a zinc plate loses electrons.*

All this experimental evidence, said Einstein, could be quite satisfactorily explained by Planck's new idea of energy quanta. A certain amount of energy, W_{Zn}, is required to pull an electron loose from the attraction of the atoms in a zinc plate. According to the old classical theories, the energy of light or ultraviolet radiation spread out in spherical waves, so the amount of energy an electron could absorb from one tiny spot on such a spreading wave front would be negligible. However, Einstein argued, the old classical picture does not represent what actually happens. The entire energy of the quantum is absorbed in one bite by a single electron. Planck's relationship, $E = h\nu$, tells how much energy there will be in a quantum of any given frequency ν.

For the zinc plate, W_{Zn} is greater than the energy associated with a quantum of visible light, so that no matter how much visible light shines on the plate, no electron will receive enough energy to break loose. This is the situation with a sheet of glass screening the arc light—ordinary window glass shuts out the invisible but highly energetic ultraviolet radiation. With the glass removed, the ultraviolet radiation from the arc, being of higher frequency than visible light and hence of proportionally higher energy, is absorbed by the electrons in the plate. The energy of a quantum of ultraviolet is greater than W_{Zn}, so the electrons can escape, carrying any leftover excess energy with them in the form of kinetic energy. With the plate negatively charged, the departing electrons are repelled, and the plate gradually loses its charge. A positively charged plate, however, will attract the electrons back as quickly as they escape, so there is in this case no loss of charge.

For a general energy relationship we need consider three terms: $h\nu$, which is the entire energy of the quantum absorbed by the electron; W, the energy required to pull the electron free from the surface; and $\frac{1}{2}mv^2$, the kinetic energy of the electron as it leaves. Simple consideration of the conservation of energy gives us:

$$h\nu - W = \tfrac{1}{2}mv^2$$

For an electron to be pulled off at all, without anything left over as KE, the $h\nu$ of the quantum must equal W, which has different values for different materials. The threshold wave lengths and frequencies at which $h\nu$ just equals W for the following three elements are:

Platinum	$\lambda = 1{,}980$ A,	or	$\nu = 1.51 \times 10^{15}$/sec
Silver	$\lambda = 2{,}640$ A,	or	$\nu = 1.13 \times 10^{15}$/sec
Potassium	$\lambda = 7{,}100$ A,	or	$\nu = 4.22 \times 10^{14}$/sec

In his classical paper on this subject, published in 1905, Einstein indicated that the observed laws of the photoelectric effect can be understood if, following the original proposal of Max Planck, one assumes that *light propagates through space in the form of individual energy packages and that, on encountering an electron, such a light quantum communicates to the electron its entire energy.*

This revolutionary assumption explains quite naturally the observed fact that the increase of the intensity of light leads to the increase of the number of photoelectrons, but not of their energy. More intense light means that more light quanta of the same kind will fall on the surface per second, and, since a single light quantum can eject one and only one electron, the number of electrons must increase correspondingly. On the other hand, by decreasing the wave

FIG. 21. *Dr. Arthur Compton, who conceived the idea that the interaction between a photon and an electron is analogous to a collision between two elastic balls. The recoiled photon has less energy and a correspondingly larger wave length, as is shown schematically in the picture.*

length of incident light we increase the frequency and, consequently, the amount of energy carried by each individual light quantum, so that in each collision with a free electron in the metal these quanta will communicate to it a correspondingly larger amount of kinetic energy.

The Compton Effect

The Planck-Einstein picture of individual energy packages, or light quanta, forming a beam of light and colliding with the electrons within matter intrigued the mind of an American physicist, Arthur Compton (Fig. 21), who, being of a very realistic disposition, liked to visualize collisions between light quanta and electrons as similar to those between ivory balls on a billiard table. He argued that, in spite of the fact that the electrons forming the planetary system of an atom are bound to the central nucleus by attractive electric forces, these electrons would behave exactly as if they were completely free if the light quanta which hit them carry sufficiently large amounts of energy. Suppose that a black ball (electron) is resting on a billiard table (Fig. 22) and is bound by a string to a nail driven into the table's surface and that a player, who does not see the string, is trying to put it into the corner pocket by hitting it with a white ball (light quantum). If the player sends his ball with a comparatively small velocity, the strong will hold during the impact and nothing will come of this attempt. If the white ball moves somewhat faster, the string may break, but in doing so it will cause enough disturbance to send the black ball in a completely wrong direction. If, however, the kinetic energy of the white ball exceeds, by a large factor, the work necessary to break the string that holds the black ball, the presence of the string will make practically no difference, and the result of the collision between the two balls will be practically the same as if the black ball were completely unbound.

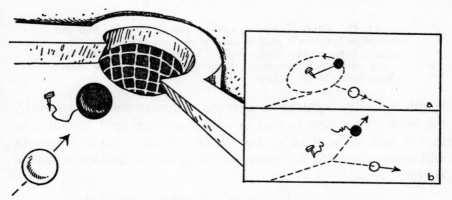

FIG. 22. *A tied-up billiard ball (black) is hit by a moving ball (white). If the white ball moves slowly (a), the effect of the string will be essential, but if it moves fast (b), the result of the collision will be the same as if the black ball were not tied at all.*

Compton knew that the binding energy of the outer electrons in an atom is comparable to the energy of the quanta of visible light. Thus, in order to make the impact overpoweringly strong, he selected for his experiments the energy-rich quanta of high-frequency X-rays. The result of a collision between X-ray quanta and (practically) free electrons can be indeed treated very much in the same way as a collision between two billiard balls. In the case of an almost head-on collision, the black ball (electron) will be thrown at high speed in the direction of the impact, while the white ball (X-ray quantum) will lose a large fraction of its energy. In the case of a side hit, the white ball will lose less energy and will suffer a smaller deflection from its original trajectory. In the case of a mere touch, the white ball will proceed practically without deflection and will lose only a small fraction of its original energy. In the language of light quanta, this behavior means that in the process of scattering, *the quanta of X-rays deflected by large angles will have a smaller amount of energy and, consequently, a larger wave length.* The experiments carried out by Compton confirmed, in every detail, the theoretical expectations and thus gave additional support to the hypothesis of the quantum nature of radiant energy.

4. The Bohr Atom

Bohr's Quantum Orbits

When Rutherford (at that time just plain Ernest Rutherford and not yet Sir Ernest or Lord Rutherford) was at the University of Manchester performing his epoch-making experiments that demonstrated the existence of the atomic nucleus, a young Danish physicist named Niels Bohr (1886–   ) came to work with him on the theoretical aspects of the atomic structure problem. Bohr (Fig. 23) was highly impressed by Rutherford's new atomic model in which the electrons revolved around the central nucleus, in very much the same way as the planets revolve around the sun, but he could not understand how such a motion could be at all possible in an atom. The planets of the solar system are electrically neutral, but atomic electrons are heavily charged with negative electricity (in fact, there is not much more to an electron than its electric charge!). It was well known from the theory of electricity that oscillating or revolving electric charges always emit electromagnetic waves. The emission of electromagnetic waves must result in the loss of energy by the emitting particle, so that the electrons in the Rutherford model were bound to spiral toward the central nucleus and fall into it when all of their rotational energy was spent on radiation.

Bohr calculated that the emission of electromagnetic waves (which in the case of the atom corresponds to light waves of different lengths) would cause the electrons forming an atomic system to lose all their energy and fall into the nucleus within one hundred-millionth of a second! Thus, on the basis of conventional mechanics and electrodynamics, the planetary system of electrons revolving around the atomic nucleus as visualized by Rutherford could not exist for more than an extremely short period of time. This was in

50

direct contradiction of the fact that atoms *do exist permanently* and
do not show any tendency to collapse. How could it possibly be?
Bohr's solution of this conflict between the conclusions of conventional mechanics and the facts of nature was straightforward and
just: *Since nature cannot be wrong, conventional mechanics must
be wrong, at least when applied to the motion of electrons within an
atom.* In making this revolutionary statement concerning the motion
of electrons within an atom, Bohr followed the precedent established
by Planck and Einstein, who had some time before declared that
the good old Huygens light waves were not what they were supposed to be according to the conventional views, but rather a bunch
of individual oscillating light quanta.

FIG. 23. *Niels Bohr and H. J. Bhabha, the chairman of the Atomic
Energy Commission of India, during the Indian Science Congress
in Bombay, January 1960. The pointing hand belongs to Mrs.
Bohr.*

It is always much easier to say that something is wrong than to
find a way to make it right, and Bohr's criticism of conventional
mechanics in the case of atomic electrons would be of no value whatsoever if he could not show a way out of the difficulty. The way he

proposed was so odd and unconventional that he kept the manuscript locked in his desk for almost two years before he decided to
send it in for publication. When this epoch-making paper finally
appeared in 1913, it sent out a shock wave of amazement through
the world of contemporary physics!

Defying the well-established laws of classical mechanics and electrodynamics, Bohr stated that in the case of the motion of electrons
within an atom the following postulatory rules must strictly hold:

I. *From all the mechanically possible circular and elliptical orbits
of electrons moving around the atomic nucleus, only a few highly
restricted orbits are "permitted," and the selection of these "permitted" orbits is to be carried out according to specially established*
rules.

II. *Circling along these orbits around the nucleus, the electrons
are "prohibited" from emitting any electromagnetic waves, even
though conventional electrodynamics says they should.*

III. *Electrons may "jump" from one orbit to another, in which
case the energy difference between the two states of motion is emitted in the form of a single Planck-Einsteinian light quantum.*

The whole thing sounded quite incredible, but it *did* permit Bohr
to interpret the regularities of spectra emitted by various atoms and
to construct a consistent theory of internal atomic structure. We will
limit our discussion here to the case of the hydrogen atom, which
contains a single electron revolving around the nucleus. Bohr's original restrictions concerning the motion of the electron in a hydrogen
atom pertained strictly to the case of circular motion and required
that the angular momentum of the electron be an integral multiple
of $h/2\pi$, where h is Planck's constant. Bohr's assumptions also de-
manded that *the "permitted" orbits be only those whose radii 2^2,
3^2, 4^2, 5^2, etc., larger than a certain minimum radius: r_0.* The set of
these "permitted" orbits is shown in Fig. 24.

Since, according to Bohr's postulate, *the radii of permitted orbits
increase as the squares of the integers,* we can conclude from the
regular laws of mechanics (or, rather, from what is left of these
laws) that *the energy of motion along these orbits decreases as the
inverse squares of the integers.*

Now, according to the second of Bohr's postulates, an electron
does not emit any radiation while moving along a given orbit but

does so when it "jumps" from one orbit to another. Consider, for example, the "jump" of an electron from the third orbit to the second one. Since the corresponding energies are proportional to $\frac{1}{3^2} = \frac{1}{9}$ and $\frac{1}{2^2} = \frac{1}{4}$, the energy difference liberated in this jump must be proportional to $(\frac{1}{4} - \frac{1}{9})$. In the case of a "jump" taking place from the fourth, fifth, etc., orbits to the second one, the corresponding energy differences are expected to be proportional to $(\frac{1}{4} - \frac{1}{16})$, $(\frac{1}{4} - \frac{1}{25})$, etc.

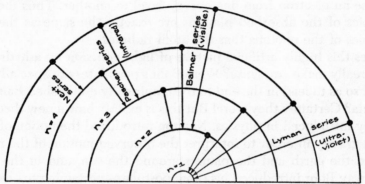

FIG. 24. *Different series of spectral lines originating in the electron transitions in a hydrogen atom. (The radii of the orbits are not to scale.)*

Remembering that, according to Bohr's third postulate, the energy liberated in such a jump is transformed directly into a single light quantum and that, according to the Planck-Einstein hypothesis, the energy of a light quantum is proportional to its frequency (i.e., $E = h\nu$), we conclude that *the frequencies of light emitted by a hydrogen atom must be proportional to $(\frac{1}{4} - 1/n^2)$ where n is an integer. But, this is exactly the "Balmer formula" for the hydrogen spectrum.* This formula states that the frequencies of the observed lines in that spectrum are exactly proportional to the difference between the inverse square of 2, i.e., $\frac{1}{4}$, and the inverse squares of 3, 4, 5, etc.

A question naturally arises about how the electron in the hydrogen atom could get up to a higher energy level in order to jump back and emit energy. Obviously, the electron can get into a higher energy orbit only by absorbing energy. This absorbed energy may come from collisions, if the gas is heated to a high temperature. It may come from the energy of an electric spark or cathode-ray tube discharge, or *it may arise from the gas absorbing, from radiation falling on it, those same frequencies that it is able to emit.* This last is the explanation of the dark lines crossing the spectrum of the sun. The highly compressed gases of the deep-lying solar photosphere emit a continuous spectrum including all frequencies. The atoms in the low-pressure upper atmosphere of the sun absorb from this continuum of radiation those photons whose energy is just exactly enough to raise an electron from one energy level to another. Thus the frequencies of the absorbed photons are exactly the same as the frequencies of the photons that the atom radiates.

Does this highly artificial picture of light emission by a hydrogen atom really make any sense? Were Bohr's postulates not specially adjusted so as to lead in the end to the empirically established Balmer's formula? Certainly they were! But this is exactly how a new theory is usually introduced in physics. Newton introduced the notion of universal gravity in order to interpret the observed motion of the moon around the earth and the planets around the sun, and in the very same way Bohr introduced his three postulates pertaining to electron motion in an atom and light emission by "jump" processes in order to interpret the observed laws of atomic line spectra. However, the criterion for the validity of any new theory in physics is not only that this theory should give a correct interpretation of the previous observations but that it also *predict* things which be later confirmed by direct experiment. In this respect, Bohr's theory of atomic structure came out with flying banners. The theory was constructed in order to interpret Balmer's formula, and this was achieved by ascribing the lines of the Balmer series to the fact that electrons "jump" from various higher orbits to the *second orbit* in the hydrogen atom. Spectral lines corresponding to the first type of jump (i.e., to the first orbit) were expected to be located in the ultraviolet part of the spectrum and were, in fact, found there by the Harvard spectroscopist, Lyman. The line corresponding to jumps to the third orbit lie in the infrared region where they were actually found by the German spectroscopist, Paschen (see Fig. 24). The fact that Bohr's atomic model, constructed especially in order to explain the Balmer series alone, leads to further conclusions that were later verified by experiment makes it a *really good theory.*

Production of X-rays

Corresponding to the single electron of the hydrogen atom, the outermost electrons of other atoms also have orbits of higher energy to which they can jump when excited by heat or strong electrical fields, or by the absorption of radiation of the proper frequency and energy. In dropping back to their normal levels, these electrons radiate frequencies characteristic of the atoms to which they belong. As in the hydrogen atom, these outer-electron frequencies are in the range of visible light, infrared, or ultraviolet. X-rays are likewise produced by electron jumps from one energy level to another, but the energy differences radiated away are enormously greater than those associated with outer electrons, and the resulting X-rays are of very high frequency.

An X-ray tube is similar in principle to a cathode-ray tube, and electrons emitted from the cathode are accelerated through a vacuum by a potential of many thousands of volts to strike against a metal anode. This bombardment is so energetic that electrons are knocked out of the *inner shells* of the atoms of the anode. When a heavy metal atom thus loses an inner electron, the vacancy is filled by one of the outer electrons falling down to take its place, and the energy differences between inner and outer electron shells are enormous, particularly for the large atoms of heavy metals. These large energy differences, by the $E = h\nu$ relationship, are radiated away as energetic photons of very high frequency.

Elliptical Quantum Orbits

Bohr's paper in which the notion of quantum orbits of atomic electrons was first introduced caused a deluge of publications all over the world, and within a few years the quantum theory of atomic structure developed into one of the most important branches of physics. The first step in this development was the generalization of Bohr's idea of circular quantum orbits in a hydrogen atom for the case of elongated elliptical orbits. This extension of Bohr's scheme was carried out by the German physicist, A. Sommerfeld, and is illustrated in Fig. 25. While retaining, unchanged, the first of Bohr's orbits, Sommerfeld added one elliptical orbit to Bohr's second orbit, two elliptical orbits to Bohr's third orbit, etc. Although the elliptical orbits added by Sommerfeld had different geometrical shapes, they nevertheless corresponded to almost the same energies as Bohr's circular orbits (same energy for 2 and 2', for 3, 3', and 3", etc.), so that Bohr's original explanation of the lines of the Balmer series in hydrogen remained unchanged.

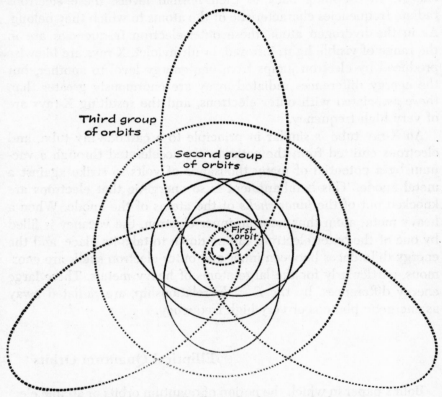

FIG. 25. *The circular and elliptical orbits in a hydrogen atom, according to Sommerfeld.*

The purpose of the modification introduced by Sommerfeld was to allow more freedom in choosing the "permitted" orbits in more complicated atoms that contain more than one electron. It was known that for sodium or potassium, for example, the lines of the emission spectrum form a series very similar to the Balmer series of hydrogen, but that in the spectrum each line consists of several closely spaced components called the "multiplicity structure." Sommerfeld explained this multiplicity structure of spectral lines as owing to the fact that, in the presence of other electrons, the energy of elliptical orbits becomes slightly different from that of the circular ones, which results in a corresponding change in the frequencies of light quanta emitted during the electron jumps from one of these orbits to the other.

The Pauli Principle

Since we are now acquainted with all the possible orbital motions of atomic electrons that are permitted by the Bohr-Sommerfeld rules, we can tackle the question of what the combined internal motion looks like in atoms that contain many electrons. Since atomic electrons have a tendency to jump from higher orbits to lower ones, emitting their excess energy in the form of light quanta, the normal state of any atom would be the state in which all atomic electrons move in a "ring around the rosy" along the first of Bohr's orbits. With atoms of increasing atomic number, this ring would become more and more crowded because it would have to accommodate more electrons and also because its radius would become smaller and smaller owing to the stronger electric attraction exercised by the central nucleus.

If this were true, the size of atoms would decrease rapidly with atomic number, and an atom of lead, for example, would be much smaller than one of aluminum. Experiment tells us that this is not so; although atomic volumes show periodic variations, they remain essentially the same throughout the periodic system of the elements. To avoid this congestion of electrons on the innermost orbit, a new postulatory restriction was apparently necessary, and it was introduced by the physicist, W. Pauli. According to the Pauli principle,* *any given quantum orbit in an atom can be occupied by no more than two electrons.* Electrons are known to rotate rapidly around their axes like little spinning tops, and the Pauli principle permits two electrons to move along the same orbit only under the condition that they spin in opposite directions.

* Called the *exclusion principle* by Pauli himself.

Electron Shells and the
Periodic System

We are now in a position to find the pattern of electron motion in the atoms of the elements. The element immediately following hydrogen is helium, the atom of which contains two electrons. If these two electrons spin in opposite directions, both can be accommodated on the first (circular) Bohr's orbit, as shown in Fig. 26a.

The next element is lithium, with three atomic electrons. Since no place is available on the first Bohr's orbit, the third electron has to be placed on the next higher energy shelf, i.e., either on the second Bohr's circular orbit or on the corresponding elliptical (Sommerfeld's) orbit. A detailed analysis of this situation indicates that there are three elliptical orbits of this type, which are identical in shape and in energy but are oriented in space in three different ways, and that the energy of motion along these elliptic orbits is slightly lower than that for the second circular orbits. Thus, the normal state of the lithium atom will be as shown in Fig 26b.

As we proceed along the natural sequence of elements, more and more electrons are placed on the second set of orbits until we reach neon, the tenth element. In neon, eight electrons are accommodated on the second shelf, and the pattern of electron motion within the atom looks as shown in Fig. 26c. This shelf of energy or, as physicists call it, "electron shell," is completely occupied, and if there are more electrons, they must be placed on the third shelf (or shell). Thus, the atom of the eleventh element, sodium, will have two completed electron shells (with 2 and 8 electrons, respectively) and one extra electron that is to be accommodated on the third energy shelf (Fig. 26d).

An atom of sodium is, in a way, similar to an atom of lithium, since in both cases there is one extra electron moving outside of a previously completed electron shell; this similarity accounts for the similarity of their chemical properties and also of their optical spectra. It goes without saying that the prototype of sodium and lithium atoms is the hydrogen atom itself.

The element following sodium is magnesium, which has two extra electrons beyond the completed shell that give it chemical properties similar to those of beryllium. It is followed by aluminum with 3 outer electrons that make this atom chemically similar to boron, and so on, until we come to argon. Argon has 18 electrons: 2 in the first shell, 8 in the second, and 8 in the third, which is a very stable configuration. The next element is potassium, which has one extra electron beyond the outer shell of argon and is the fourth member of the H, Li, Na sequence of chemically similar elements.

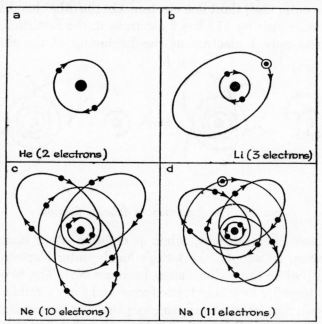

FIG. 26. *How the electron shells in more and more complex atoms are filled. As the atomic number increases, the electron shells shrink, because of the increased nuclear electric charge, so that the size of the atoms remains on the average constant. Electrons forming the beginning of a new shell are indicated with a circle around them.*

We see that the combination of the Bohr-Sommerfeld notion of quantum orbits and Pauli's principle concerning the orbital cohabitance of atomic electrons leads to a simple and complete explanation of the periodic properties of the elements.

Chemical Valence

This view of atomic shell structure gives us a simple explanation of the nature of the chemical valence of different elements. We can show, on the basis of the quantum theory, that atoms which have an almost completed shell have a tendency to take in extra electrons in order to finish this shell and that atoms which have just the beginning of a new electron shall have a tendency to get rid of these extra electrons. For example, chlorine (atomic number 17) has 2 electrons in the first shell, 8 in the second, and 7 in the third, which makes the outer shell short one electron. On the other hand, a sodium atom (atomic number 11) has 2 electrons in the first shell, 8 in the second, and only 1 electron as the beginning of the third shell.

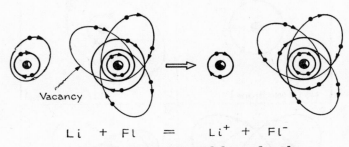

Li + Fl = Li$^+$ + Fl$^-$

FIG. 27. *The formation of lithium flouride.*

Under these circumstances, when a chlorine atom encounters a sodium atom, it "adopts" the latter's lonely outer electron and becomes Cl$^-$, while the sodium atom becomes Na$^+$. The two ions are now held together by electrostatic forces and form a stable molecule of table salt. Similarly, an oxygen atom that has two electrons missing from its outer shell (atomic number $= 8 = 2 + 6$) tends to adopt two electrons from some other atom and can thus bind two monovalent atoms (H, Na, K, etc.) or one bivalent atom, such as magnesium (atomic number $= 12 = 2 + 8 + 2$), which has two electrons to lend. An example of chemical binding of this kind is shown in Fig 27. It also becomes clear why the noble gases, which have all their shells completed and have no electrons to give or to take, are chemically inert.

5. Wave Nature
of Particles

De Broglie Waves

Although Bohr's theory of atomic structure was immensely successful in explaining a large number of known facts concerning atoms and their properties, the three fundamental postulates underlying his theory remained quite inexplicable for a long period of time. The first step in the understanding of the hidden meaning of Bohr's discrete quantum orbits was made by a Frenchman, Louis de Broglie, who tried to draw an analogy between the set of discrete energy levels that characterize the inner state of atoms and the discrete sets of mechanical vibrations that are observed in the case of violin strings, organ pipes, etc. "Could it not be," de Broglie asked himself, "that the optical properties of atoms are due to some kind of standing waves enclosed within themselves?" As a result of these considerations, de Broglie came out with his hypothesis that *the motion of electrons within the atom is "guided" by a peculiar kind of waves which he called "pilot waves."* According to these unconventional views, each electron circling around an atomic nucleus must be considered as being accompanied by a standing wave that runs around and around the electronic orbit. If this is true, the only orbits that would be possible are those whose lengths are an integral multiple of the wave length of the corresponding de Broglie wave.

Figure 28 shows the application of de Broglie's idea to the first three orbits of the Bohr hydrogen atom. In order to have n complete wave lengths (λ_n) fit into the circumference of the nth orbit, de Broglie had to assume that

$$\lambda_n = \frac{h}{mv}$$

The above relationship states de Broglie's fundamental hypothesis,

that *the wave length of the wave associated with a moving particle
is equal to Planck's quantum constant divided by the momentum of
the particle.*

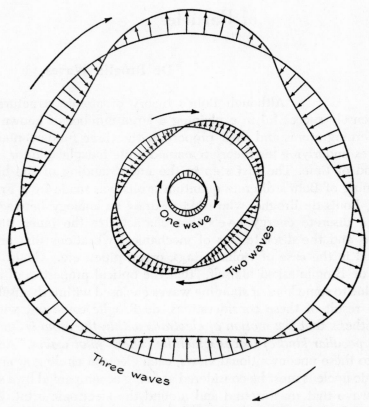

FIG. 28. *De Broglie's waves as applied to the first three orbits of
Bohr's atom.*

Although we have justified this by considering an electron in a
Bohr atom, if electrons are really accompanied by these mysterious
de Broglie waves while moving along the circular orbits within an
atom, the same must be true for the free flight of electrons as observed in free electron beams. And, if the motion of electrons in
the beams is "piloted" by some kind of waves, we should be able
to observe the phenomena of *interference* and *diffraction* of elec-

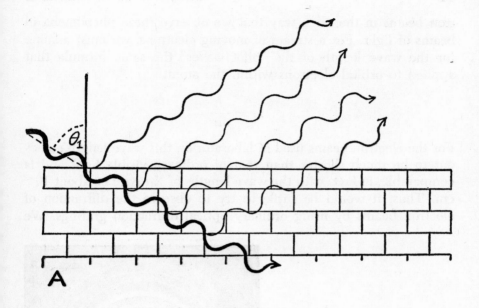

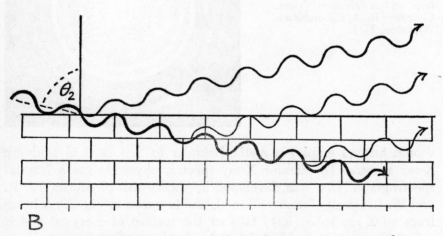

FIG. 29. *Reflection of X-rays or de Broglie waves from a crystal. The layers of molecules are represented symbolically by bricks in a wall. In A the angle of incidence θ_1 is such that the neighboring waves are out of phase, leading to destructive interference. In B the angle θ_2 is such that all waves are almost in phase, resulting in high intensity.*

tron beams in the same way that we observe these phenomena in beams of light. For a stream of moving electrons, we must assume for the wave length of the "pilot waves" the same formula that applied to orbital electrons within the atom:

$$\lambda = \frac{h}{mv}$$

For the electron beams used in laboratories, this wave length comes out to be much shorter than that of ordinary visible light and is comparable, in fact, with the wave lengths of X-rays, i.e., about 10^{-8} cm. Thus, it would be futile to try to observe the diffraction of electron beams by using ordinary optical diffraction gratings. We

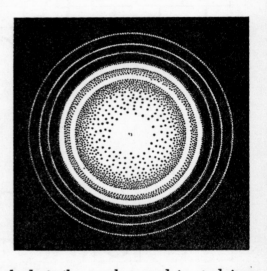

FIG. 30. *The diffraction pattern of an electron beam.* Courtesy RCA Laboratories, Princeton, N. J.

should instead employ a method similar to that used in studying X-ray spectra. To examine X-ray spectra, physicists use a "crystal spectrograph" that was developed by the British physicists, W. H. and W. L. Bragg (father and son), and is shown in Fig. 29. A beam from an X-ray tube (left) falls on the surface of a crystal and is reflected successively from the molecular layers that form the crystalline surface. Depending on the angle, the wavelets reflected from different layers may be "in phase" with each other or "out of phase," thus leading to the intensification or to the reduction of the intensity of the reflected beam.

Two American physicists, C. J. Davisson and L. H. Germer, used a similar arrangement in their experiments on electron diffraction, the only difference being that the beam of X-rays was replaced by a beam of electrons, which was accelerated by passing it through an electric field between two grids. The result of Davisson and Germer's experiment gratified their expectations, and they obtained a genuine diffraction pattern of an electron beam (Fig. 30) with the wave length corresponding exactly to the value predicted by the de Broglie theory.

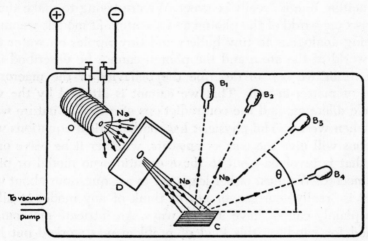

FIG. 31. *O. Stern's experiment demonstrating the diffraction of a molecular beam. A beam of sodium atoms from the oven, O, is passed through a diaphragm, D, and falls on a crystal, C. The atoms reflected from the crystal in different directions are collected in bottles, B_1, B_2, B_3, etc., and their amounts are measured. The results show a strong maximum in the direction required by the ordinary law of reflection, and a number of secondary maxima corresponding to a diffraction pattern.*

A few years later, a German physicist, O. Stern, repeated the experiments of Davisson and Germer by using a molecular beam of hydrogen molecules and helium atoms (Fig. 31) instead of an electron beam and found that the diffraction phenomenon exists in that case, too. Thus, it became quite evident that in material particles as small as atoms and electrons, the basic ideas of classical Newtonian mechanics should be radically changed by introducing the notion of "pilot waves" guiding material particles in their motion.

The once definite distinction between waves and particles seems to have broken down. There are many sorts of interference experiments in which light shows itself to be unquestionably a wave phenomenon; yet in the photoelectric effect it concentrates all its energy on a single electron, as though it were a bullet-like particle. And now electrons and atoms, so surely particles, behave in some experiments as though they were waves.

The wave aspect and the particle aspect seem to be so mutually contradictory that it is quite natural to ask which one is "really" correct for a beam of light or an electron. The modern physicist will say that neither one is "really" correct. We are trying to make the submicroscopic world of the photon and the atom fit models we imagine as being analogous to tiny bullets and tiny ripples on water tanks. The world of the atom and the photon cannot be described in the same terms we use to describe the behavior of the macroscopic world of matter-in-bulk. That we cannot is attested by the wave-particle dilemma, and the contradictions of a similar nature we run into when we try. The physicist has mathematical equations whose solutions will give the correct answers, whether it be wave or particle that is involved—but to these equations no model or picture is connected. We must either learn not to ask questions about which model is "really" correct, or not to think of any model at all. We quite plainly cannot have it both ways. An intricate mathematical method for handling this kind of problem was worked out by an Austrian physicist, E. Schroedinger, and it represents the subject matter of an important but rather difficult branch of modern theoretical physics known as *wave mechanics*.

The Uncertainty Principle

Now things seem to be going from bad to worse. First, we had Bohr's "quantized orbits" that looked like railroad tracks along which the electrons were running around the atomic nucleus. Then these tracks were replaced by mysterious "pilot waves" that were supposed to provide "guidance" for the electrons in their orbital motion. It all seemed to be against common sense, but, on the other hand, these developments of the quantum theory provided us with the most exact and most detailed explanation (or description) of the properties of atoms—their spectra, their magnetic fields, their chemical affinities, etc. How could it be? How could what was, at first sight, a nonsensical picture lead to so many positive results? Here we repeat that modern physics extends its horizons far beyond the everyday experience upon which all the common-sense ideas of classical physics were based. We are thus bound to find striking deviations from our conventional way of thinking and must be prepared to encounter facts that sound quite paradoxical to our ordinary common sense. In the case of the theory of relativity, the revolution of thought was brought about by the realization that space and time are not the independent entities they were always believed to be, but are the parts of a unified space-time continuum. In the quantum theory we encounter a non-conventional concept of *the minimum amount of energy*, which, although of no importance in the large-scale phenomena of everyday life, leads to revolutionary changes in our basic ideas concerning motion in tiny atomic mechanisms.

Let us start with a very simple example. Suppose we want to measure the temperature of a cup of coffee but all we have is a large thermometer hanging on the wall. Clearly, the thermometer will be inadequate for our purpose because when we put it into the cup it will take so much heat from the coffee that the temperature shown will be considerably less than that which we want to measure. We can get a much better result if we use a small thermometer that will show the temperature of the coffee and take only a very small fraction of its heat content. The smaller the thermometer we use for this measurement, the smaller is the disturbance caused by the measurement. In the limiting case when the thermometer is "infinitely small," the temperature of the coffee in the cup will not be affected at all by the fact that the measurement was carried out. The common-sense concept of classical physics was that this is always the case in whatever physical measurements we are carrying out, so that we can always compute the disturbing effect of whatever gadget is used for the measurement of some physical quantity and get the exact value we want. This statement certainly applies to all large-scale measurements carried out in any scientific or engineering laboratory, but it fails when we try to stretch it to such tiny mechanical systems as the electrons revolving around the nucleus of the atom. Since, according to Max Planck and his followers, energy has "atomic structure," *we cannot reduce the amount of energy involved in the measurement below one quantum,* and making exact measurements of the motion of electrons within an atom is just as impossible as measuring the temperature of a demitasse of coffee by using a bulky bathtub thermometer! But, whereas we can always get a smaller thermometer, it is absolutely impossible to get less than one quantum of energy.

A detailed analysis of the situation indicates that *the existence of the minimum portions of energy prohibits us from describing the motion of atomic particles in the conventional way by giving their successive positions and velocities.* Both of these quantities can be known only within certain limits, which although negligibly small for the large-scale object, become of paramount importance within tiny atomic mechanisms. This uncertainty in the knowledge of the coordinate x and the velocity v of a particle can be expressed mathematically by writing $x \pm \Delta x$ and $v \pm \Delta v$, which means that all we can say is that the value of the coordinate lies somewhere between $x - \Delta x$ and $x + \Delta x$, and that the value of the velocity lies somewhere between $v - \Delta v$ and $v + \Delta v$. The German physicist, W. Heisenberg, has shown that the quantities Δx and Δv are subject to the relation:

$$\Delta x \times \Delta v = \frac{h}{m}$$

where m is the mass of the particle and h Planck's quantum constant which has the numerical value 6.77×10^{-27}. The smaller m is, the more restricting is Heisenberg's uncertainty relation. If we apply it, for example, to a particle weighing 1 mg (10^{-3} gm), we find that:

$$\Delta x \times \Delta v = 10^{-24}$$

which may mean that if the uncertainty of the position is ± 0.000000000001 cm, the uncertainty of the velocity is $\pm 0.000000\cdot 000001$ cm/sec. Clearly, such small uncertainties are of no importance! However, using for m the mass of an electron (about 10^{-27} gm), we obtain:

$$\Delta x \times \Delta v = 1$$

which indicates that there may be an uncertainty of ± 1 cm in the position and ±1 cm/sec in the velocity. These uncertainties are large enough to make the classical picture of the orbital motion of atomic electrons completely invalid. De Broglie's "pilot waves" give us a new way of describing the motion of atomic particles in which, instead of speaking about their trajectories, *we speak only about the probability of finding the particle in one or another location in space.* In fact, *the intensity of these waves gives us directly this probability.*

Anti-Particles

Up until about a quarter of a century ago, physicists recognized only two kinds of elementary particles from which matter was supposedly built. They were *protons*, the relatively massive particles carrying a positive electric charge, and the much lighter negatively charged *electrons*. But this simple picture was distorted in 1929 by a British physicist, P. A. M. Dirac (Fig. 32), who was at that time busy trying to reconcile the basic principles of the quantum theory with those of Einstein's theory of relativity. On the basis of very abstract theoretical considerations, Dirac came to the conclusion that, apart from the "ordinary" electrons which rotate around atomic nuclei or fly through vacuum tubes, there must also exist an incalculable multitude of "extraordinary" electrons distributed uniformly throughout what one usually calls empty space. Although, according to Dirac's views, each unit volume of vacuum is packed to capacity with these "extraordinary" electrons, their presence escapes any possible experimental detection. The "ordinary" electrons studied by physicists and utilized by radio engineers are those few excess particles that cause an "overflow" of "Dirac's ocean" (Fig. 32, right), which is formed by the "extraordinary" particles, and they thus can be observed individually. If there is no such "overflow" nothing can be observed, and we call the space empty. The nearest simple analogy that may serve to clarify these rather unorthodox views is that of a deep water fish who never rises to the surface of the ocean. Of course, fish in general do not possess much in the way of brains, but even if they were as intelligent as modern theoretical physicists they would find it difficult to conceive of the idea of a surrounding medium of water provided this medium is completely uniform and (as it is in the case of "Dirac's ocean") frictionless. In a similar way, Dirac's ocean surrounding us on all sides and extending into infinity in all directions remains unobserv-able to us. In a sense, Dirac's theory brings us back to the old-fashioned idea of the "all-penetrating world ether," but in an en-tirely new fashion.

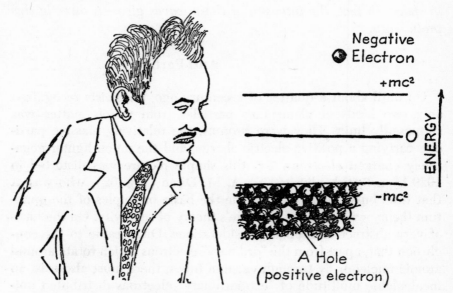

FIG. 32. *Dr. P. A. M. Dirac, who conceived the idea that "empty space" is actually tightly packed with electrons of negative mass that are inaccessible to any physical observation. We can observe an electron only when it is raised into the region of positive energy (above on the right). The removal of an electron from the continuous distribution forms a "hole" (below on the right) which represents a "positive" electron.*

In addition to having the property of not being observable by any physical means, these "extraordinary" electrons possess, according to Dirac, a "negative inertial mass," which means that when they are pushed in one direction by any physical force they move in exactly the opposite direction. Of course, for a conventional physicist the idea of a "negative mass" seems just as nonsensical as the idea of a vacuum tightly packed by extraordinary electrons, and during the first couple of years after its publication, Dirac's paper was sub-jected to all kinds of criticism. The criticism stopped abruptly in

1931, however, when an American physicist, Carl Anderson, confirmed by direct observation the existence of the new particles predicted by Dirac's theory.

We have said above that, because of their uniform distribution, the "extraordinary" electrons forming Dirac's ocean are invisible to observation, but what happens if one of these particles is absent, leaving in its place an empty "hole" (Fig. 32.)? This "hole" in the uniform distribution of negatively charged particles represents the *lack of a negative charge,* which is equivalent to the *presence of a positive charge.* Thus, the electrical instruments used in our physical laboratories would register this "hole" as a positively charged particle with the same numerical value of charge as an ordinary electron, but with the opposite sign. The reader will recall that the notion of "holes" in the uniform distribution of electrons in semiconductors led to a successful explanation of their properties. But, whereas in that case the notion of a "hole" can be readily visualized on the basis of an ordinary picture of the electrical nature of matter, Dirac's "holes" belong to a much more abstract physical picture.

It is also easy to see that when experimentalists study the motion of such a "hole" under the action of any external physical force, they will ascribe to it an ordinary positive mass. Returning to our intelligent deep water fish, imagine that it observes a series of air bubbles rising to the surface from a sunken submarine. Being accustomed to seeing objects in the water moving downward and sinking toward the bottom under the action of the forces of gravity, our fish would be surprised to see these silvery spheres move in the opposite direction; if our fish were intelligent enough, he might be inclined to ascribe to these unusual rising objects a "negative mass." For Dirac's ocean of "extraordinary" negative electrons possessing a negative mass, we conclude that a "hole" in this distribution must possess a mass opposite to that of the particles forming it, i.e., a positive mass. Thus, through *double negation,* we find that the *"holes" in Dirac's ocean must behave as ordinary particles carrying a positive electron charge and a positive mass.* They are called *antielectrons, positive electrons,* or simply *positrons.*

From what has been said, we can conclude that in order to form a positron we have to remove a negative electron from its place in Dirac's ocean. But when this electron is removed from the uniform distribution of the negative electric charge, it becomes observable as an ordinary negatively charged particle. Thus, *the positive and negative electrons always must be formed in pairs.* We often call this process *the creation of an electron pair,* which is not quite correct because the pairs of electrons are not

FIG. 33. *A drawing showing an electron pair produced by cosmic rays in a metal plate as seen in a cloud chamber.*

created from nothing but are formed at the expense of the energy spent in carrying out the process of their formation. According to Einstein's famous law of the equivalence of mass and energy $\left(E = Mc^2 \text{ or } M = \dfrac{E}{c^2} \right)$, the energy necessary to produce two electron masses is equivalent to about 1.64×10^{-6} ergs. Thus, if we irradiate matter with gamma rays of this and higher energies, we should be able to induce the formation of pairs of positive and negative electrons. The electron pairs discovered by Anderson were produced in atmospheric air, and also in metal plates placed in a detecting cloud chamber, by the high-energy gamma radiation that is associated with the cosmic rays which fall on the earth from interstellar space (Fig. 33). Following this discovery, physicists learned to produce electron pairs by irradiating different materials by the high-energy gamma rays that are emitted by natural radioactive substances.

The opposite of the "creation" of an electron pair is the "annihilation" of a positive electron in a collision with an ordinary negative electron. According to the above-described picture, the annihilation process occurs when an ordinary negative electron, which moves "above the rim" of the completely filled Dirac's ocean, finds a "hole" in the distribution and falls into it. In this process the two individual particles disappear, giving rise to gamma radiation with a total energy equivalent to the vanished mass radiating from the place of encounter. Dirac's original theory of "holes" not only predicted the existence of positive electrons before their experimental discovery but also gave an excellent mathematical apparatus for calculating the probabilities of the formation of electron pairs under different circumstances, as well as the probability of their annihilation in casual encounter. All the predictions of this theory stand in perfect agreement with experimental evidence.

Anti-Protons and
Anti-Neutrons

Ever since the experimental confirmation of Dirac's theory of anti-electrons, physicists have been interested in finding the *anti-protons* that should be the particles of proton mass carrying a negative electric charge, i.e., *negative protons*. Since a proton is 1,840 times heavier than an electron, its formation would require a correspondingly higher input of energy. It was expected that a pair of negative and positive protons should be formed when matter is bombarded by atomic projectiles carrying not less than 4.4 billion electron-volts of energy. With this task in mind, the Radiation Laboratory of the University of California in Berkeley and the Brookhaven National Laboratory on Long Island, New York, started construction of the gigantic electron accelerators—*Bevatron* on the West Coast (Fig. 34) and *Cosmatron* on the East Coast—that were supposed to speed up atomic projectiles to the energies necessary for the proton-pair production. The race was won by the West Coast physicists who announced in October, 1955, that they had observed negative protons being ejected from targets bombarded by 6.2 Bev (billion electron-volt) atomic projectiles. As is usual in this kind of complicated experimental research, the work was done by a team, in this case of four people: O. Chamberlain, E. Segré, C. Wiegand, and T. Ypsilantis.

The main difficulty in observing the negative protons formed in the bombarded target was that these protons were expected to be accompanied by tens of thousands of other particles (heavy mesons) also formed during the impact. Thus, the negative protons had to be filtered out separated from all the other accompanying particles. This was achieved by means of a complicated "labyrinth" formed by magnetic fields, narrow slits, etc., through which only the par-

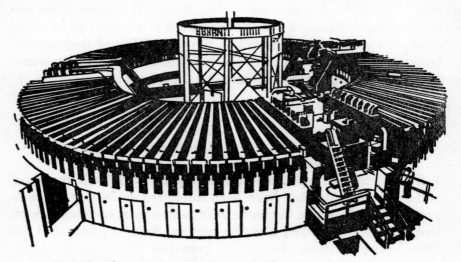

FIG. 34. *The giant accelerator at the University of California known as the Bevatron. It was this machine that first enabled scientists to detect anti-protons and anti-neutrons.*

ticles possessing the expected properties of anti-protons could pass. When the swarm of particles coming from the target (located in the bombarding beam of the Bevatron) was passed through this "labyrinth," only the negative protons were expected to come out through its opposite end. When the machine was set into operation, the four experimentalists were gratified to observe the fast particles coming out at a rate of about one every six minutes from its rear opening. As further tests have shown, the particles were genuine negative protons formed in the bombarded target by the high-energy Bevatron beam. Their mass was found to have a value of 1,840 electron masses, which is known to be the mass of an ordinary positive proton.

Just as the artificially produced positive electrons get annihilated in passing through ordinary matter containing a multitude of ordinary negative electrons, negative protons are expected to get annihilated by encountering positive protons in the atomic nuclei with which they collide. Since the energy involved in the process of proton–anti-proton annihilation exceeds, by a factor of almost two thousand, the energy involved in an electron–anti-electron collision, the annihilation process proceeds much more violently, resulting in a "star" formed by many ejected particles.

The proof of the existence of negative protons represents an excellent example of an experimental verification of a theoretical prediction concerning properties of matter, even though at the time of its proposal the theory may have seemed quite unbelievable. It was followed in the fall of 1956 by the discovery of *anti-neutrons*, i.e., the particles that stand in the same relation to ordinary neutrons as negative protons do to positive ones. Since in this case the electric charge is absent, the difference between neutrons and anti-neutrons can be noticed only on the basis of their mutual annihilation ability.

6. Natural Radioactivity

Discovery and Early Progress

The discovery of radioactivity in 1896, like that of many other unsuspected aspects of physics, was purely accidental. The French physicist, A. H. Becquerel (1852–1908), was interested at that time in the phenomenon of fluorescence, the ability of certain substances to transform ultraviolet radiation that falls on them into visible light. In one of the drawers of his desk, Becquerel kept a collection of various minerals that he was going to use for his studies, but, because of other pressing matters, the collection remained untouched for a considerable period of time. It happened that in the drawer there also were several unopened boxes of photographic plates, and one day Becquerel used one of the boxes in order to photograph something or other. When he developed the plates he was disappointed to find that they were badly fogged as if previously exposed to light. A check on the other boxes in the drawer showed that they were in the same poor condition, which was difficult to understand since all the boxes were sealed and the plates inside were wrapped in thick black paper. What could have been the cause of this mishap? Could it have something to do with one of the minerals in the drawer? Being of inquisitive mind, Becquerel investigated the situation and was able to trace the guilt to a piece of uranium ore labeled "Pitchblende from Bohemia." One must take into account, of course, that at that time uranium was not in vogue as it is today. In fact, only a very few people had ever heard about this comparatively rare and not very useful chemical element.

But the ability of uranium compounds to fog photographic plates through a thick cardboard box and a layer of black paper rapidly brought this obscure element to a prominent position in physics.

The existence of penetrating radiation that can pass through layers of ordinarily opaque materials, as if they were made of clear glass, was a recognized fact at the time of Becquerel's discovery. In fact, only a year earlier, in 1895, a German physicist, Wilhelm Roentgen (1845–1923), discovered, also by sheer accident, what are now known as X-rays, which could penetrate cardboard, black paper, or the human body equally well. But, whereas X-rays could be produced only by means of special high-voltage equipment shooting high-speed electrons at metallic targets, the radiation discovered by Becquerel was flowing steadily, without any external energy supply, from a piece of uranium ore resting in his desk. What could be the origin of this unusual radiation? Why was it specifically associated with the element uranium and, as was found by further studies, with two other heavy elements, thorium and actinium?

The early studies of the newly discovered phenomenon, which was called *radioactivity*, showed that the emission of this mysterious radiation was completely unaffected by physical and chemical conditions. One can put a radioactive element into a very hot flame, or dip it into liquid air, without the slightest effect on the intensity of the radiation it emits. No matter whether we have pure metallic uranium or its chemical compounds, the radiation flows out at a rate proportional to the amount of uranium in the sample. These facts led the early investigators to the conclusion that the phenomenon of radioactivity is so deeply rooted in the interior of the atom that it is completely insensitive to any physical or chemical conditions to which the atom is subjected.

Becquerel's discovery attracted the attention of the Polish-born Madame Marie Sklodowska Curie (1867–1934), wife of the French physicist, Pierre Curie. She suspected that the radioactivity of uranium ore might, to a large extent, be due to some other chemical element, much more active than uranium, which might, however, be present in uranium ore in very small quantity. Being an experienced and hard-working chemist, Madame Curie decided to separate this hypothetical element from uranium ore by a painstaking method known as "chemical fractioning." Carloads upon carloads of pitchblende from Bohemia went through Madame Curie's chemical kitchen where careful processing was taking place, and only the fractions of the material emitting radiation were retained. Her work culminated in 1898 with a brilliant success: she obtained a few milligrams of a pure element that was a million times more radioactive than uranium itself. She christened the new element "radium," and its number in the periodic system of elements was 88. Another radioactive element discovered by Madame Curie was even more active than radium and she named it "polonium" in honor of her native country. The study of radioactivity carried on by many investigators at the turn of the century led to the discovery of many other radioactive elements carrying such strange names as uranium X_1, ionium, radium emanation, etc. The puzzling process of radioactivity was interpreted by the British physicists, Soddy and Rutherford, to be the result of the spontaneous transformations of the elements near the end of the periodic system into other elements, in fulfillment of the dreams of medieval alchemists.

Alpha, Beta, and Gamma Rays

In their early studies of radioactive substances, Becquerel and his followers found that their radiation consisted of three different components:

Alpha rays, composed of fast-moving helium nuclei. Since these nuclei carry a double positive charge and have a mass of four atomic units, the result of alpha transformation is to convert the element that emits the α-particle into another element which has an atomic number smaller by two and an atomic weight smaller by four.

Beta rays, composed of fast-moving negative electrons. Since a loss of negative charge is equivalent to a gain of positive charge, the atomic number of the resulting element increases by one. The atomic weight, however, does not change because of the negligibly small mass of the electron.

Gamma rays, which are associated both with α and β transformations, were shown to be short electromagnetic waves similar to X-rays, emitted by atomic nuclei in the process of α- or β-particle ejection.

It is quite easy (in principle, at least) to separate these three types of radiation when they are emitted from a small piece of

material containing a mixture of radioactive elements. If we drill
a small hole in a block of lead, which is a good absorber of radiations of all kinds, and place a speck of radioactive material at the
bottom of the hole, a narrow, well-defined beam of radiation will
be emitted from the top of the hole (Fig. 35). If this beam is

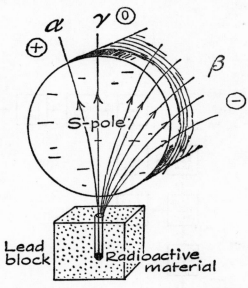

FIG. 35. *The separation of alpha, beta, and gamma radiation by passage through an
electric field.*

passed through a strong electric field between a pair of parallel
plates, the single beam will be separated into its three components,
as shown. The same results will follow if, instead of the electric
field, the beam is passed through a strong magnetic field perpendicular to the plane of the drawing.

Families of Radioactive Elements

Radioactivity, observed by Becquerel in uranium and its compounds, turned out to be a composite effect that was owing to the
presence of a large number of radioactive elements, including radium and uranium themselves. In fact, studies by the British physicist, Soddy, and his famous collaborator, Rutherford, showed that
this mixture contained over a dozen individual elements.

In the uranium family, which also includes radium, uranium plays the role of the head of the family and, being very long-lived, produces numerous children, grandchildren, great-grandchildren, etc. The genealogy of the uranium family is shown in Fig. 36. An atom

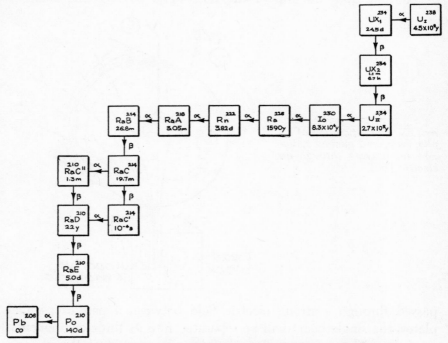

FIG. 36. *The uranium-radium family. The numbers at the bottom of the squares give the half life periods in years (y), days (d), hours (h), minutes (m), and seconds (s). Notice the forking (αβ or βα) at RaC.*

of UI, the father of the family ($_{92}U^{238}$; atomic number 92, mass number 238), emits an α-particle and is transformed into an atom of so-called UX₁. Since the α-particle ($_2He^4$) carried away two units of charge and four units of mass, UX₁ has an atomic number of 90 (92 − 2) and a mass number of 234 (238 − 4). The element with atomic number 90 is thorium, and the so-called UX₁ is really an isotope of thorium, $_{90}Th^{234}$. The nuclear equation for this transformation is:

$$_{92}U^{238} \rightarrow {}_2He^4 + {}_{90}Th^{234}$$

The next step is the emission of a β-particle by UX₁, which turns it into UX_2. The emission of a β-particle (an ordinary electron, $_{-1}e^0$) carried away a unit of negative charge, which is the same as adding a positive charge to the nucleus, and thus the atomic number is *increased* by one; the mass number is not changed by β-emission. Thus our UX_1 nucleus, which is really $_{90}Th^{234}$, becomes $UX_2(_{91}Pa^{234})$:

$$_{90}Th^{234} \rightarrow _{-1}\beta^0 + _{91}Pa^{234}$$

The next step is the emission of another β-particle by UX_2 which turns it into UII with the same atomic number as UI, but four units of mass lighter. The following α-emission leads to ionium (atomic number 90, atomic weight 230), etc., etc. After seven α-emissions and six β-emissions, we arrive at a polonium atom, which emits an eighth α-particle and turns into an atom of lead (Pb) with atomic number $92 - 8 \times 2 + 6 \times 1 = 82$, and atomic weight $238 - 8 \times 4 = 206$. The nuclei of Pb^{206} are stable and no further radioactive transformations take place.

Genealogically speaking, the thorium and actinium families are very similar to that of uranium and terminate with stable lead isotopes Pb^{208} and Pb^{207}, respectively. Besides these radioactive families, which include the heaviest elements of the periodic system and are transformed by a series of intermittent α- and β-decays into isotopes of lead, a few lighter elements also go through a one-step transformation. These include samarium (Sm^{148}), which emits α-rays and turns into stable Nd^{144}, and two β-emitters, potassium (K^{40}) and rubidium (Rb^{87}), which turn into stable isotopes of calcium (Ca^{40}) and strontium (Sr^{87}).

Decay Energies

The velocities of α-particles emitted by various radioactive elements range from 0.98×10^9 cm/sec for samarium 148 to 2.06×10^9 cm/sec for ThC'; these velocities correspond to kinetic energies of from 3.2 to 14.2×10^{-6} erg. The energies of β-particles and γ-quanta are somewhat smaller but of the same general order of magnitude. These energies are considerably higher than the energies encountered in ordinary physical phenomena. For example, the kinetic energy of atoms in thermal motion, at such a high temperature as 6,000°K (surface temperature of the sun), is only 1.25×10^{-12} erg., i.e., several million times smaller than the energies involved in radioactive decay.

In speaking about the energies liberated in radioactive transformations, nuclear physicists customarily use a special unit known as the *electron-volt*. This unit is defined as *the energy gained by a particle carrying one elementary electric charge* (no matter whether it is an electron or any singly charged positive or negative ion) *when it is accelerated through an electric field with a potential difference of 1 volt*. Thus, the electrons accelerated in J. J. Thomson's tube, with 5,000 volts applied between the anode and cathode, acquire by this definition an energy of 5,000 electron-volts. On the other hand, the energy of a doubly charged oxygen ion, O^{++}, accelerated through the same potential difference will be 10^4 electron-volts, since the electric force acting on the ions, and consequently the work done by it, is twice as large. Remembering that the value of an elementary charge on an electron, proton, or any singly charged ion is 1.60×10^{-19} coulomb, and that a volt is one joule-coulomb, *we find that one electron-volt of energy is 1.60×10^{-19} joule, or 1.60 $\times 10^{-12}$ erg*. Another unit commonly used in nuclear work is the Mev, which stands for "million electron-volts," and the Bev which stands for "billion electron volts."

Half Lifetimes

As was mentioned above, the process of natural radioactive decay is ascribed to some kind of intrinsic instability of the atomic nuclei of certain chemical elements (especially those near the end of the periodic table). From time to time this results in a violent breakup and the ejection from the nucleus of either an α-particle or an electron. The nuclei of different radioactive elements possess widely varying degrees of internal instability.

In some cases (such as uranium), radioactive atoms may remain perfectly stable for billions of years before breaking up; in other cases (such as RaC'), they can hardly exist longer than a small fraction of a second. The breakup of unstable nuclei is a purely statistical process, and we can speak of the "mean lifetime" of any given elements in just about the same sense as insurance companies speak of the mean life expectancy of the human population. In the case of human beings and other animals, the chance of decaying (i.e., dying) remains fairly low up to a certain age and becomes high only when the person grows old, but radioactive atoms have the same chance of breaking up no matter how long it has been since they were formed (by the decay of the previous element in the family). Since

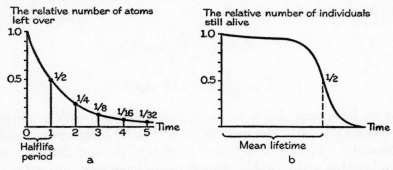

FIG. 37. *A comparison of the survival curve for radioactive atoms and for living individuals.*

radioactive atoms begin to die out at the very moment of their birth, the decrease of their number with time is different from the corresponding decrease of the number of living individuals (Fig. 37a and b). In the latter case, the curve of surviving individuals runs first almost horizontally and becomes steep later only when the organism begins to wear out, but the radioactive decay curve is steep all the time.

The number of decaying radioactive atoms is proportional to the number of atoms available but is quite independent of the age of these atoms.

The situation resembles that existing on a battlefield where any of the soldiers can be killed with equal chances any day of the campaign, while the cases of natural death, which depend on the soldier's age, are of very small importance. The time period during which the initial number is reduced to one-half is known as the *half-life period* of the element. At the end of twice that period, only a quarter of the original amount will be left; at the end of three half-life periods, only one-eighth will be left, etc. From the arguments above, we see a simple way to formulate mathematically the amount of a decaying element that is left after any number of half lives. If we start out with an amount of N_0 of some radioactive material, after n half lives have passed there will be left an amount N:

$$N = N_0 \times \left(\frac{1}{2}\right)^n$$

The gas radon, for example, has a half life of 3.8 days. If we start out with 5 mg of radon, how much will be left after a month? A month is $30/3.8 = 8$ half lives, and:

$$N = 5 \times \left(\frac{1}{2}\right)^n$$

$$= 5 \times \frac{1}{256} = 0.02 \text{ mg left}$$

As we have seen above, various elements possess widely different life times (Fig. 36). The half life of U^{238} is 4.7 billion years, which accounts for its presence in nature in spite of the fact that all atoms of both stable and unstable elements may have been formed about five billion years ago, but the half life of radium is only 1,620 years; hence the 200 mg of radium separated in 1898 by Marie and Pierre Curie now contains only 195 mg. The short-lived atoms of RaC' exist, on the average, for only 0.0001 sec between the moment they are formed by β-emission of RaC and their transformation into RaD atoms.

Uranium-Lead Dating

The decay of radioactive elements and its complete independence of physical and chemical conditions gives us an extremely valuable method for estimating the ages of old geological formations. Suppose we pick up a rock from a shelf in a geological museum that is marked as belonging to the late Jurassic era; i.e., to the period of the earth's history when gigantic lizards were the kings of the animal world. Geologists can tell approximately how long ago this era was by studying the thicknesses of various prehistoric deposits and by comparing them with the estimated rates of the formation of sedimentary layers, but the data obtained by this method are rather inexact. A much more exact and reliable method, based on the study of the radioactive properties of igneous rocks, was proposed by Joly and Rutherford in 1913 and soon became universally accepted in historical geology. We have seen above that uranium is the father of all other radioactive elements belonging to its family and that the final product of all these disintegrations is a stable isotope of lead, Pb^{206}.

The igneous rock of the Jurassic era that now rests quietly on a museum shelf must have been formed as a result of some violent volcanic eruption of the past when molten material from the earth's interior was forced up through a crack in the solid crust and flowed down the volcanic slopes. The erupted molten material soon solidified into rock that did not change essentially for millions of years. But, if that piece of rock had a small amount of uranium imbedded in it, as rocks often do, the uranium would decay steadily, and the lead resulting from that decay would be deposited at the same spot. The longer the time since the solidification of the rock, the larger would be the relative amount of the deposited lead with respect to the leftover uranium. Thus, by measuring the uranium-to-lead ratio in various igneous rocks, we can obtain very exact information concerning the time of their origin and the age of the geological deposits in which they were found.

Similar studies can be carried out by using the rubidium inclusions in old rocks and measuring the ratio of leftover rubidium to the deposited strontium. This method has an advantage over the uranium-lead method because we deal here with a single transformation instead of the long sequence of transformations in the uranium family. In fact, one of the members of the uranium family is a gas (radium emanation or radon) and could partially diffuse away from its place of their formation, thus leading to an underestimation of the age of the rocks.

Carbon Dating

Apart from the above-mentioned natural radioactive elements, which are presumably as old as the universe itself, we find on the earth a number of radioactive elements that are being continuously produced in the terrestrial atmosphere by cosmic ray bombardment. Among these, the most interesting is the heavy isotope of carbon,

C^{14}, which is produced from atmospheric nitrogen by a high-energy neutron impact (N^{14} + neutron → C^{14} + proton) and incorporated into the molecules of atmospheric carbon dioxide. Since plants use atmospheric carbon dioxide for their growth, radioactive carbon is

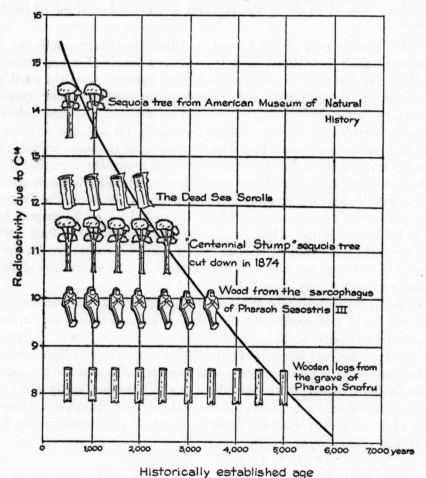

FIG. 38. *The radioactivity, due to C^{14}, of various old objects as the function of their age, measured by Dr. W. Libby. Each symbol represents 500 years of age.*

incorporated into each plant's body, making all plants slightly radioactive throughout their life.

As soon as a tree is cut or falls down and all of the metabolic processes stop in its body, however, no new supply of C^{14} is available and the amount of radioactive carbon in the wood gradually decreases at time goes on. Since the half life of C^{14} is 5,700 years, the decay will last for many milleniums, and by measuring the ratio of C^{14} to the ordinary C^{12} in old samples of wood we are able to estimate rather exactly the dates of origin. The studies in this direction were originated by an American physicist, W. Libby (1908–), and are playing the same role in the exact dating of ancient human history as the measurement of the uranium-lead ratio in the dating of the history of our globe. The measurement of C^{14} radioactivity in old samples of wood is a very delicate matter since it is usually much weaker than the radioactivity of the background surrounding the object (the experimenter himself has a higher C^{14} concentration than the piece of wood he is studying) and cosmic rays. Thus, the sample under investigation must be heavily shielded, and a very

TABLE 5

1. Lake mud from Knock nac ran, Ireland.	Age: $11,310 \pm 720$
2. Wood from the bottom deposits of Lake Kickapoo, Illinois.	Age: $13,842 \pm 780$
3. Charcoal from Lascaux Cave near Les Eyzies, France.	Age: $15,516 \pm 900$
4. Wood from the woody layer at the bottom of the sand and gravel deposit at Dyer, Indiana.	Age: $18,500 \pm 500$

sensitive counter must be used. In Fig. 38 we give a few examples of the measured and expected concentrations of radioactive carbon in various wooden objects of known age. Using these data and measuring the C^{14} concentration in wooden objects of unknown age, we can easily estimate their ages. Some examples of such estimates are given in Table 5.

Measurements of the C^{14} content of trees felled by the glaciers have established that the last glaciation of northern United States was much more recent (about 10,000 years ago) than had been previously supposed.

Tritium Dating

Another interesting method of dating by the use of radioactive materials, which was also worked out by W. Libby, utilizes the radioactivity of tritium, i.e., the heavy unstable isotope of hydrogen with atomic weight 3. Tritium is also produced in the terrestrial atmosphere under the action of cosmic radiation and is precipitated to the surface by rains. However, tritium's half life is only 12.5 years,

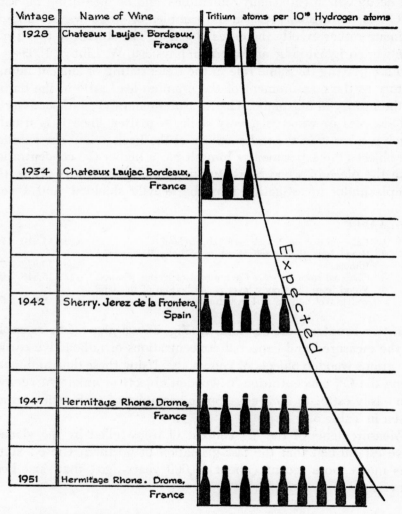

Vintage	Name of Wine	Tritium atoms per 10^{18} Hydrogen atoms
1928	Chateaux Laujac. Bordeaux, France	
1934	Chateaux Laujac. Bordeaux, France	
1942	Sherry. Jerez de la Frontera, Spain	
1947	Hermitage Rhone. Drome, France	
1951	Hermitage Rhone. Drome, France	

FIG. 39. *The agreement between the calculated and the expected relationship of radioactivity vs. age in various wines.*

so that all age measurements involving this isotope can be carried out only for comparatively recent dates. The most interesting application of the tritium dating method may be in the study of the movements of water masses, both in ocean currents and in underground waters, since by taking samples of water from different locations and from different depths, we can tell by their tritium content how long ago this water came down in the form of rain.

Samples of old water are more difficult to collect than samples of old wood, and Libby resolved this problem by analyzing the tritium content in wine of different vintages, originating in different countries. Regrettably, an entire case of a fine wine must be used for each measurement and is rendered undrinkable in the process. But the agreement with the expected tritium content was in all cases excellent, as demonstrated in Fig. 39.

7. Artificial Nuclear Transformations

Splitting of Atomic Nuclei

After Rutherford became completely persuaded that the radioactive decay of heavy elements is due to the intrinsic instability of their atomic nuclei, his thought turned to the possibility of producing the artificial decay of lighter and normally stable nuclei by subjecting them to strong external forces. True enough, it was well known at that time that the rates of radioactive decay are not influenced at all by high temperatures or by chemical interactions, but this could be simply because the energies involved in thermal and chemical phenomena are much too small as compared with the energies involved in the nuclear disintegration phenomena. Whereas the kinetic energy of thermal motion (at a few thousand degrees) as well as the chemical energy of molecular binding are of the order of magnitude of only 10^{-12} erg, the energies involved in radioactive decay are of the order of 10^{-6} erg, i.e., a million times higher. Thus, in order to have any hope of a positive outcome, the light stable nuclei must be subjected to a much stronger external agent than just a high temperature or a chemical force, and the bombardment of light nuclei by high-energy particles ejected from the unstable heavy nuclei was the natural solution of the problem.

Following this line of reasoning, Rutherford directed a beam of α-particles emanating from a small piece of radium against a thin layer of nitrogen gas and observed, to his complete satisfaction, that besides the α-particles that passed the layer and were partially scattered in all directions, there were also a few high-energy protons (i.e., the nuclei of hydrogen) that were presumably produced in the collisions between the onrushing α-projectiles and the nuclei of nitrogen atoms. This conclusion was later supported by cloud chamber photographs, as we will discuss in the next section. The capture of an α-particle followed by the ejection of a proton increases the atomic number of the nucleus in question by one unit ($+2 - 1 = +1$) and its mass by three units ($+4 - 1 = +3$), transforming the original nitrogen atom $_7N^{14}$ into an atom $_8O^{17}$ of a heavier isotope of oxygen. We can express this reaction by the nuclear formula:

$$_7N^{14} + {_2}He^4 \rightarrow {_8}O^{17} + {_1}H^1$$

Following this original success, Rutherford was able to produce the artificial transformation of other light elements, such as aluminum, but the yield of protons produced by α-bombardment rapidly decreased with increasing atomic number of the target material, owing to the increase in electrostatic repulsion of the α-particle by the greater $+$ charge of the larger nuclei, and he was not able to observe any ejected protons for elements heavier than argon (atomic number 18).

Photographing Nuclear Transformations

The study of nuclear transformations was facilitated by the ingenious invention of still another Cavendish physicist, C. T. R. Wilson. This device, known as the "Wilson chamber" or "cloud chamber," permits us to obtain a snapshot showing the tracks of individual nuclear projectiles heading for their targets and also the tracks of various fragments formed in the collision. It is based on the fact that whenever an electrically charged fast-moving particle passes through the air (or any other gas), it produces ionization along its track. If the air through which these particles pass is saturated with water vapor, the ions serve as the centers of condensation for tiny water droplets, and we see long thin tracks of fog stretching along the particles' trajectories. The scheme of a cloud chamber is shown in Fig. 40. It consists of a metal cylinder, C, with a transparent glass top, G, and a piston, P, the upper surface of which is painted black. The air between the piston and the glass top is initially saturated with water (or alcohol) vapor, generally by a coating of moisture on top of the piston. The chamber is brightly

illuminated by a light source, S, through a side window, W. Suppose
now that we have a small amount of radioactive material on the end
of a needle, N, which is placed near the thin window, O.

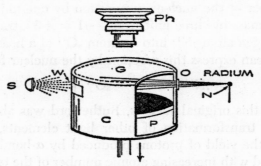

FIG. 40. *A cloud chamber.*

The particles that are ejected by the radioactive atoms will fly
through the chamber ionizing the air along their paths. However,
the positive and negative ions produced by the passing particles re-
combine rapidly into neutral molecules. Suppose, however, that the
piston is pulled rapidly down for a short distance. The rapid expansion of the air will cause it to cool, and the already saturated
air now becomes supersaturated with moisture which will condense
into water droplets. In order to condense, however, the droplets
need centers of some sort around which to form. The natural condensation of raindrops takes place on dust particles, tiny salt crystals,
or ice crystals. In *cloud-seeding*, airplanes scatter minute crystals of
silver iodide to encourage the condensation of rain droplets.

In the cloud chamber, however, there is no dust, and the droplets
condense on the ions (as the next best thing) that have been formed
along the path of the speeding particles. Thus the tracks of the particles that passed by just before, or just as, the piston was pulled
down will show up as trails of microscopic water droplets. The tracks
of α-particles are quite heavy, since the massive doubly charged α
ionizes the air strongly. The track of a proton is less strongly marked,
and along the path of an electron the ions and hence the droplets are
much more sparse. In much of the present cloud chamber work, an
intense magnetic field is created within the chamber, so the charged
particles are deflected into curved paths. By measuring the curva-
ture shown on the photographs, we can compute the speed and
energy of the particles.

Figure 41 is a sketch of the classical cloud chamber photograph, taken in 1925 by P. T. M. Blackett that shows the collision of an incident α-particle with the nucleus of a nitrogen atom in the air which fills the chamber. The long thin track going almost backward is that of a proton ejected in that collision. It can be easily recog-

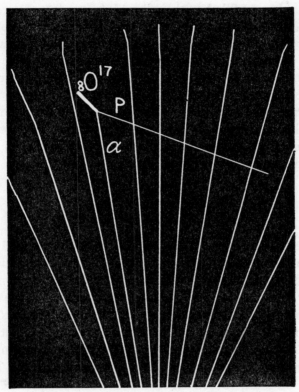

FIG. 41. *Sketch of the first cloud chamber photograph, taken by Blackett, of nuclear disintegration. The long thin track at upper right is that of a proton that has been ejected from a nitrogen hit by an α-particle. The short thicker track, at upper left, is that of an oxygen nucleus formed in the collision. All other α-particles shown in the sketch lost their energy before they had a chance to hit a nucleus.*

nized as a proton track because protons are four times lighter than α-particles and carry only one-half as much electric charge; therefore they produce fewer ions per unit length of their path than α-particles. The short heavy track belongs to the nucleus $_8O^{17}$ formed in the process of collision.

Bubble Chambers

In recent years, the "bubble chamber" has been developed to supplement the work of the cloud chamber. Although the general principle of its operation is the same as that of the cloud chamber, the bubble chamber is filled with a liquid (often propane and, more recently, liquid hydrogen) which is kept exactly at its boiling-point temperature. A slight expansion will reduce the pressure on the liquid, and bubbles of vapor will form on the ions which have been produced in the liquid by passing particles. The bubble chamber has a great advantage when the collision events to be observed are relatively rare. In the closely packed atoms of a liquid, many more nuclear collisions will occur than in a gas, and the observer will stand a much better chance of photographing what he is looking for than he would with a cloud chamber.

First Atom Smashers

Since the only massive projectiles emitted by the nuclei of natural radioactive elements are α-particles, i.e., the nuclei of helium, it was desirable to develop a method for the artificial production of beams formed by other atomic projectiles, particularly beams of high-energy protons. According to theoretical considerations, the ease with which a bombarding particle penetrates into the structure of a bombarded atomic nucleus depends on the atomic number (i.e., the nuclear electric charge) of the element in question. The larger the atomic number, the stronger is the electric repulsive force opposing the approach of α-particles to the nucleus, and, consequently, the smaller are the chances of a demolishing collision. Since protons carry only one-half of the electric charge carried by an α-particle, they were expected to be much better as atomic projectiles and to be able to smash atomic nuclei of light elements even when moving with only 1 Mev of energy. Rutherford asked John Cockcroft to construct a high-tension machine that would accelerate protons to the energy of 1 million electron-volts, and, within a couple of years, the first "atom smasher" was constructed by Cockcroft and his associate, E. T. S. Walton. Directing the beam of 1-Mev protons at a

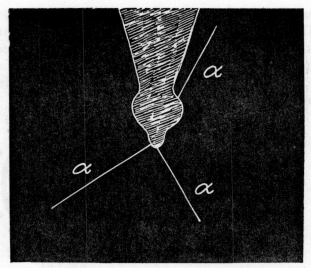

FIG. 42. *Sketch of a cloud chamber photograph, after P. Dee and C. Gilbert, of three α-particles resulting from the break-up of a boron nucleus under the impact of an artificially accelerated proton.*

lithium target, Cockcroft and Walton observed the first nuclear transformation caused by artificially accelerated projectiles. The equation of this reaction is:

$$_3Li^7 + {}_1H^1 \rightarrow 2\,{}_2He^4$$

If we use boron instead of lithium as the target, the reaction will be:

$$_5B^{11} + {}_1H^1 \rightarrow 3\,{}_2He^4$$

and the three α-particles formed in this collision fly apart as shown in Fig. 42.

The "Van de Graaff"

Cockcroft and Walton's atom smasher, which was based on the electric transformer principle, gave rise to a series of ingenious devices for producing high-tension beams of atomic projectiles. The *electrostatic atom smasher* constructed by R. Van de Graaff (1901-   ) and usually called by his name, is based on a classical principle of electrostatics, according to which an electric charge communicated to a spherical conductor is distributed entirely on its surface. Thus, if we take a hollow spherical conductor with a small hole in its surface, insert through this hole a small charged conductor attached to a glass stick, and touch the inside surface of the sphere (Fig. 43a), the charge will spread out to the surface of the big sphere.

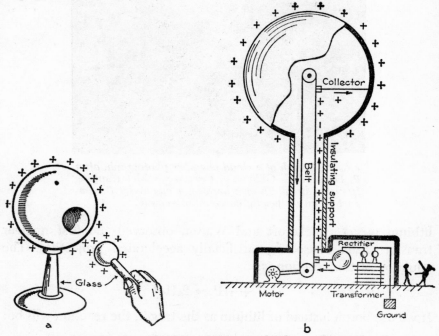

FIG. 43. *The principle (a) and the actual scheme (b) of Van de Graaff's high-tension machine.*

Repeating the operation many times, we will be able to communicate to the large conductor any desirable amount of electricity and raise its electric potential as high as desired (or, at least, until the sparks start jumping between the conductor and the surrounding walls).

In the Van de Graaff atom smasher (Fig. 43b), the small charged ball is replaced by a continuously running belt that collects electric charges from a source at the base and deposits them on the interior surface of the large metallic sphere. The high electric potential developed in this process is applied to one end of an accelerating tube in which the ions of different elements are speeded up to energies of many millions of electron-volts.

The Cyclotron

Another popular atom smasher, invented by E. O. Lawrence (1901–1958), is based on an entirely different principle and utilizes the multiple acceleration of charged particles moving along a circle

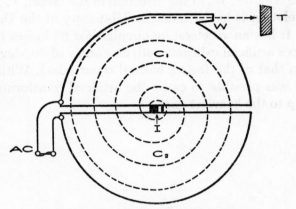

FIG. 44. *The principle of the cyclotron.*

in a magnetic field. The principle of the *cyclotron* is shown in Fig. 44. It consists essentially of a circular metal chamber cut into halves, C_1 and C_2, and placed between the poles of a very strong electromagnet. The half-chambers, C_1 and C_2 are connected with a source of alternating high potential, *AC*, so that the electric field along the slit separating them periodically changes its direction. The ions of the element to be used as atomic projectiles are injected in the center of the box, *I*, at a comparatively low velocity, and their trajectories are bent into small circles by the field of the magnet. The gimmick of the cyclotron is that, for a given magnetic field, the period of revolution of an electrically charged particle along its circular trajectory is independent of the velocity with which that particle is moving. Since the increase in the radius of the path and the length of the circular trajectory is exactly proportional to the increase in velocity, the time necessary for one revolution remains the same.

If things are arranged in such a way that the period of revolution of the ions injected into the field of the magnet is equal to the period of alternating tension produced by the AC source, the particles arriving at the boundary between the two half-chambers, C_1 and C_2, will be subject each time to an electric force acting in the same direction that the particles are moving. Thus, each time the ion passes through that boundary it will be given additional acceleration and its velocity will gradually increase. Gathering speed, the ions will move along an unwinding spiral trajectory and will finally be ejected through the window, W, in the direction of the target, T. The largest existing cyclotron is in the radiation laboratory of the University of California. It has an accelerating circular box 60 inches in diameter and produces artificial α-beams with an energy of 40 Mev (4.5 times higher than that of the fastest natural α-particles). With this atom smasher, it was possible to cause the artificial transformation of all elements up to the heaviest ones.

8. The Structure
of the
Atomic Nucleus

Nuclear Constituent Particles

As was mentioned earlier, the fact that the atomic weights of isotopes of different elements are very closely represented by integral numbers strongly suggests that atomic nuclei are formed by adding together the nuclei of hydrogen atoms, i.e., protons. But if the atomic nuclei were formed exclusively by proton aggregates, they would have a much larger electric charge than that actually observed. For example, the nucleus of the oxygen atom has a mass very close to that of 16 protons, but carries only 8 elementary units of positive charge. It follows that 8 of the 16 hydrogen nuclei that combine to form the nucleus of oxygen have lost their positive charge, i.e., have turned into neutrons. Thus, the composition of the oxygen nucleus can be written as:

$$_8O^{16} = 8 \text{ protons} + 8 \text{ neutrons}$$

Similarly, we may write for the composition of the nucleus of the principal isotope of iron:

$$_{26}Fe^{56} = 26 \text{ protons} + 30 \text{ neutrons}$$

and, for the principal isotope of uranium:

$$_{92}U^{238} = 92 \text{ protons} + 146 \text{ neutrons}$$

The assumption that atomic nuclei are aggregates of protons and neutrons is substantiated by the fact that both protons and neutrons are observed to be ejected from atomic nuclei in the processes of artificial nuclear transformations. According to this assumption, α-particles emitted by various radioactive elements are composite units formed by two protons and two neutrons each. It is believed that α-particles do not exist inside atomic nuclei as such, but are built up from nuclear protons and neutrons just before their emission. Conversely, an α-particle entering the nucleus breaks up into two protons and two neutrons, which then mix with the other nuclear constituent particles.

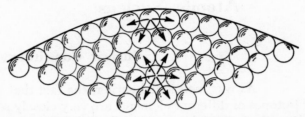

FIG. 45. *The mutual attraction of molecules in a liquid that produces the effect of surface tension.*

We notice that, whereas in the case of light nuclei the number of neutrons is equal to the number of protons, the number of neutrons exceeds the number of protons for heavier elements; the number of neutrons is 20 per cent larger in iron and 50 per cent larger in uranium. Neutrons outnumber protons in the heavier nuclei because the protons, being positively charged, repel each other, and their relative number must be reduced in order to secure the stability of the nucleus.

The Nucleus as a
Fluid Droplet

It is clear that the forces which hold the nucleus in one piece cannot be of a purely electric nature, since half of the nuclear particles (neutrons) do not carry any electric charge, whereas the other half (protons) are all positively charged, thus repelling one another and contributing to nuclear disruption rather than to stability. In order to understand why the constituent parts of the nucleus stick closely together, we must assume that there exist between them forces of some kind, attractive in nature, which act on uncharged neutrons as well as on positively charged protons. These forces that make them adhere, irrespective of the nature of the particles involved, are generally known as *cohesive forces* and are encountered, for example, in liquids, where they hold together the separate molecules and lead to the familiar phenomenon of surface tension.

The action of surface tension is explained by the forces illustrated graphically in Fig. 45. A particle deep inside a liquid is subjected to attractive forces from the other particles surrounding it on all sides, so that the total resultant of all these pulls is exactly zero. On the other hand, a particle located on the surface has all its neighbors on only one side, so that their combined attraction results in a strong force pulling the particle inward. Since every particle located on the surface is pulled inward by other particles, the liquid will have a general tendency to reduce its free surface to the smallest possible value, which explains the spherical shape assumed by any liquid drop that is not acted upon by any external forces; it is well known that the sphere is the geometrical figure that possesses the smallest surface for a given total volume.

The assumption that the forces acting between the constituent particles of the nucleus are similar to those acting between the molecules of any ordinary liquid leads to the *droplet model* of an atomic nucleus, according to which different nuclei are considered as minute droplets of a universal *nuclear fluid*.

The first important consequence of the nuclear-droplet theory is the conclusion that the volumes of different atomic nuclei must be proportional to their masses, since the density of the fluid always remains the same, regardless of the size of the droplet which it forms. This conclusion is completely confirmed by direct measurements of nuclear radii which show that, throughout the entire sequence of elements, the radii of atomic nuclei vary as the cube roots of their masses. Thus, the radii of the atomic nuclei of oxygen and lead, which have masses of 16 and 206 atomic mass units, respectively, are measured to be 3×10^{-13} and 7×10^{-13} cm. From these figures we see that the lead nucleus is 13 times as massive as the oxygen nucleus; hence it has a volume 13 times as great. The cube root of 13 is 2.35, which is exactly the ratio of the nuclear radii. Remembering that the actual mass of the hydrogen atom is 1.66×10^{-24} gm, we find that the nuclei of oxygen and lead have masses of 2.66×10^{-23} gm and 3.42×10^{-22} gm. Since the volumes of these two nuclei are 1.13×10^{-37} and 1.44×10^{-36} cm³, we obtain in both cases a value of nearly 2.4×10^{14} gm/cm³ for the density of nuclear fluid. This is a very high density indeed! If the nuclear fluid, which is dispersed through space in the form of minute droplets surrounded by rarefied electronic envelopes, could be collected to form a continuous material, 1 cc of it would weigh 240 million tons.

Along with its almost unbelievably high density, nuclear fluid possesses a correspondingly high surface tension. The surface tension of a liquid is characterized by the force acting on a unit length of the free surface boundary. For example, if we spread a soap film over the area enclosed by a U-shaped wire, with a piece of straight wire put across it, the forces of surface tension will pull the cross wire in an attempt to reduce the surface of the film. Measuring this force and dividing it by the length of the cross wire, and also by the factor 2 because the soap film has two surfaces and consequently acts with a double force, we arrive at the value of the surface tension force acting on the unit length. The surface tension of water, for example, is known to be about 75 dynes/cm at room temperature. The surface tension of nuclear fluid is found to be 93,000,000,000,000,000,000 dynes/cm, which is as nice and big a number as the one which describes the density of the fantastic nuclear fluid. A nuclear film attached to a wire 1 cm long would support the weight of 1 billion tons.

The value of the surface tension force immediately determines the amount of energy that is connected with any change of the total free surface of a fluid. In fact, any increase of the free surface requires work to be done against the surface tension forces; a decrease of the surface area will, on the contrary, liberate a certain amount of energy. Numerically, the amount of energy in ergs per cm^2 of surface area is given by the same number as the surface tension force, in dynes/cm, and is equal to 9.3×10^{19} ergs/cm^2, so that, in order to calculate the total surface energy of the nucleus, we have to multiply the surface area by the above number.

Instead of expressing the surface energy per unit of surface area, we can more conveniently express it per single nuclear particle located on the surface. Since the diameter of a neutron or proton is about 3.2×10^{-13} cm, each of them occupies on the nuclear surface an area of about 10^{-25} cm^2, so that there are 10^{25} particles per cm^2. Dividing the above total surface energy per cm^2 by the number of the particles per cm², we find that there is about 9×10^{-6} erg, or about 5 million electron-volts, of energy per particle. This represents the energy that would be necessary to remove one nucleon from the surface of the nucleus against the forces of cohesion, and is analogous to the heat of evaporation per molecule for ordinary liquids.

Mass Defect and Nuclear Binding Energy

In comparing the masses of various atomic nuclei with the masses of the protons and neutrons from which they are formed, we always find a slight discrepancy. For example, in the case of oxygen, we have:

$$
\begin{array}{llll}
8 \text{ neutrons} & = 8 \times 1.00898 & = & 8.07184 \\
8 \text{ protons} & = 8 \times 1.00759 & = & 8.06072 \\
8 \text{ electrons} & = 8 \times 0.00055 & = & 0.00440 \\
\hline
& & & 16.13696
\end{array}
$$

which may be compared with the atomic weight of oxygen, or 16.00000.*

It was necessary to add the 8 electrons because atomic weights always include the weight of the atomic electrons in their values. Since the number of atomic electrons is always equal to the number of protons in the nucleus, it may be more convenient, in figuring nuclear discrepancies, to use the hydrogen atom instead of the proton, as this automatically includes the proper number of electron masses. For oxygen, we could have written:

$$
\begin{array}{llll}
8 \text{ neutrons} & = 8 \times 1.00898 & = & 8.07184 \\
8 \text{ hydrogens} & = 8 \times 1.00814 & = & 8.06512 \\
\hline
& & & 16.13696
\end{array}
$$

Thus, by either method, the oxygen nucleus is seen to be lighter than its constituents by 0.13696 units of atomic weight, or atomic mass units (amu).

* This figure is an exact integer not because of any property of the oxygen atom, but because atomic weight figures are based on a scale in which the atomic weight of the principal isotope of oxygen is assumed to be exactly 16.

Similarly, in the case of the principal isotope of iron, we have:

$$\begin{array}{rcl}
30 \text{ neutrons} & = 30 \times 1.00898 = & 30.26940 \\
26 \text{ hydrogens} & = 26 \times 1.00814 = & 26.21164 \\
\hline
& & 56.48104 \text{ amu}
\end{array}$$

which is to be compared with the exact value of 55.9571 for the atomic weight of Fe^{56}. Here we find that the atomic weight of Fe^{56} is 0.5239 amu smaller than the combined masses of its components.

The explanation of this so-called mass defect[†] is based on Einstein's law of the equivalence of mass and energy. When a nucleus is being formed from individual protons and neutrons, large amounts of nuclear energy are set free, just as chemical energy is liberated in the form of heat during the formation of water molecules from hydrogen and oxygen atoms. This energy possesses a certain mass, which is carried away and makes the resultant nucleus correspondingly lighter. Since the unit of atomic weight (1/16 of the actual weight of the oxygen atom) equals 1.66×10^{-24} gm, its energy equivalent is:

$$1.66 \times 10^{-24} \times (3 \times 10^{10})^2 = 1.48 \times 10^{-3} \text{ erg or 932 Mev}$$

Dividing the total binding energy of the composite nucleus by the total number of protons and neutrons forming it, we obtain a mean binding energy per particle.[‡]

In Fig. 46 we give a plot of the nuclear binding energy per particle against atomic weight. We notice that this binding energy per particle (which has rather large values for light nuclei) decreases with the atomic weight, reaches a minimum in the neighborhood of $A = 50$, and then begins to increase again toward the heavy elements.

The reason for this behavior of binding energy is the fact that there are two opposing forces acting within the nucleus:

1. The nuclear attractive forces that attempt to hold the nuclear constituent particles together.

2. Electrostatic repulsive forces between protons that push them apart.

[†] In Aston's original definition, *mass defect is the difference between the exact value of the atomic weight and the nearest integral number*. However, for theoretical considerations it is more rational to use the definition of mass defect as given here.

[‡] If we use Aston's definition of mass defect, the mass defect per nuclear particle is known as the *packing fraction*.

In the case of lighter elements, nuclear attraction between the constituent particles prevails over the electrostatic repulsion between the protons, and the increase of the total number of particles leads

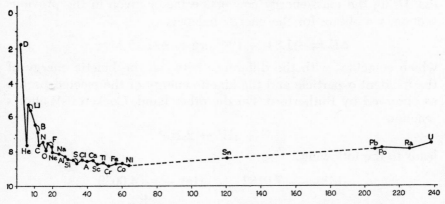

FIG. 46. *The binding energy per nucleon vs. atomic mass number.*

to the strengthening of their mutual binding. In the case of heavier elements, the effect of repulsion between protons becomes more noticeable, weakening the average binding between the nuclear particles.

Mass Defect and Nuclear Reactions

The exact knowledge of the atomic weights of the isotopes permits us to evaluate the energy balance of various nuclear reactions, since the mass equivalent of the liberated or absorbed nuclear energy must enter into the equation of the conservation of mass during the transformation. Thus, in the case of Rutherford's original reaction:

$$_7N^{14} + _2He^4 \rightarrow _8O^{17} + _1H^1$$

The sums of masses of the atoms entering the reaction and those resulting from it are, respectively:

$_7N^{14}$ —— 14.00753		$_8O^{17}$ —— 17.00450	
+		+	
$_2He^4$ —— 4.00386		$_1H^1$ —— 1.00813	
18.01139		18.01263	

The combined mass of the reaction products is larger than the combined mass of the atoms entering into the reaction, by 0.00124 atomic mass units, indicating that some energy is lost in this process. Using the mass-energy conversion factor given in the previous section, we obtain for the energy balance:

$$\Delta E = -1.84 \times 10^{-6} \text{ erg} = -1.15 \text{ Mev}$$

which coincides with the difference between the kinetic energy of the incident α-particle and the kinetic energy of the ejected proton as observed by Rutherford. On the other hand, Cockcroft-Walton's reaction:

$$_3\text{Li}^7 + {}_1\text{H}^1 \rightarrow 2{}_2\text{He}^4$$

leads to the following:

$$_3\text{Li}^7 \underline{\quad\quad} 7.0182 \qquad {}_2\text{He}^4 \underline{\quad\quad} 4.0039$$
$$+ \qquad\qquad\qquad\qquad +$$
$$_1\text{H}^1 \underline{\quad\quad} 1.0081 \qquad {}_2\text{He}^4 \underline{\quad\quad} 4.0039$$
$$\overline{8.0263} \qquad\qquad \overline{8.0078}$$

In this case the difference is +0.0191 atomic mass units, corresponding to an energy liberation of 1.8×10^{-5} erg or 17.7 Mev per reaction.

Nuclear Shell Model

As we explained in the earlier discussion of the Bohr atom (under Electron Shells and the Periodic System), the regular repetition of the chemical properties of atoms arranged in order of increasing atomic number is due to the formation of the consecutive electron shells in the electronic envelopes of the atoms. Similar periodic changes are also observed in the case of atomic nuclei, manifesting themselves in the behavior of nuclear binding energies, magnetic properties, ability to participate in various nuclear reactions, etc. Inspecting the binding energy curve in Fig. 45, we notice that, instead of being smooth, it contains kinks (at O, Cr, and other points), indicating that certain irregularities in the internal nuclear structure are present. Another example of these irregularities is shown in Fig. 47, where the ability of different nuclei to capture neutrons (capture cross sections) is plotted against atomic weight.

We notice that the regular increase of this ability with increasing atomic weight is interrupted by sharp minima (at He, O, and Cr).

Detailed studies of these and other irregularities of nuclear properties led to the conclusion that they always occur when either the number of neutrons or the number of protons is one of the following numbers: 2, 8, 14, 20, 28, 50, 82, 126, which represent the number of particles at which nuclear shells are completed. These so-called

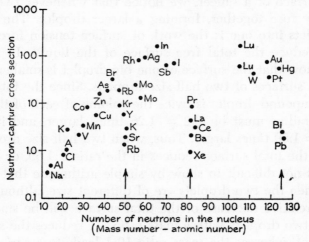

FIG. 47. *A cross-section graph of neutron capture.*

magic numbers are analogous to the sequence of numbers: 2, 10, 18, 36, 54, etc. (atomic numbers of the rare gases), that characterize the periodic system of chemical elements and that represent the number of electrons at which atomic shells are completed. The abnormally small neutron-capture cross sections for the elements with completed neutron shells (Fig. 47) are analogous to the chemical inertness of the rare gas atoms that possess completed electron shells.

There are, however, two important differences between the shell structure of nuclei and the shell structure of atoms. In atoms, one system of shells accommodates the electrons of the atomic envelope, but in nuclei there are two independent sets of shells: one for neutrons and one for protons. Another difference lies in the fact that, whereas the electron shells in the atom are geometrically separated, nuclear shells apparently interpenetrate each other and so can be distinguished only by their different energies.

Fusion and Fission

In considering atomic nuclei of different chemical elements as minute droplets of universal nuclear fluid, we may expect that these nuclear droplets will behave in about the same way as droplets of ordinary liquid. In observing droplets of, let us say, mercury rolling on the surface of a saucer, we notice that whenever two droplets meet they fuse together, forming a larger droplet. The fusion of two droplets into one is the work of surface tension forces, which tend to reduce the total free surface of the liquid. In fact, it is easy to show that the surface of one big droplet is smaller than the combined surfaces of two half-size droplets. Since the total volume of the compound droplet is twice the volume of each of the smaller ones, its radius must be $\sqrt[3]{2} = 1.26$ times larger, and its surface $(1.26)^2 = 1.59$ times larger. Thus, when two half-size droplets fuse into one, the total surface reduces in the ratio 2:1.59, or by 20 per cent. It is not difficult to show by simple arithmetic that the same is true when the two droplets are of different size, although in this case the relative decrease of the total surface will be smaller. The fusion of two droplets with a mass ratio 3:1 reduces the surface by 19 per cent, whereas the mass ratio 10:1 leads to a surface reduction of only 13 per cent. Thus, the fusion of two droplets into one always leads to the liberation of surface energy and always takes place spontaneously whenever two droplets come into contact. If the surface tension forces were the only forces acting in atomic nuclei, any two nuclei would fuse together, liberating nuclear energy.

However, the situation changes quite considerably if we take into account that, apart from surface tension forces, electric forces of repulsion are also present in the nuclei. In contrast to ordinary liquids, a nuclear fluid is always electrically charged, since about one-half of its constituent particles are protons. The electric repulsion between the nuclear charges acts in the opposite direction to the surface tension forces and tends to disrupt larger droplets into smaller ones. In order to calculate the change of electric energy connected with the fission of a nucleus into two halves, we must make use of the fact that the electrical energy of a charged sphere is proportional to the square of its charge divided by its radius.

Since each of the two resultant droplets has one-half of the original charge and their radii are 1.26 times smaller than that of the original droplet, the electric energy of each will be $(\frac{1}{2})^2 \times 1.26 = 0.315$ times that of the original big droplet. The combined electric energy of two halves will be only 0.63 of the original value. Thus we conclude that electrostatic forces act in the opposite direction to the surface tension forces, favoring nuclear fission rather than fusion.

With both kinds of forces present, the answer to the question whether nuclear energy will be liberated in fusion or fission depends on the relative strength of the two forces. For the nuclei in which surface tension forces are stronger than electrostatic forces, fusion is an energy-liberating process. If, however, the reduction of electric energy over-balances the increse of surface energy, the fission process is to be expected. If we proceed along the sequence of elements from the lighter nuclei to the heavier ones, the surface energy, which is determined by the total surface of the nucleus, increases comparatively slowly, being proportional to the two-thirds power of the atomic weight (because of the constancy of nuclear density). On the other hand, electric energy increases approximately as the square of the nuclear charge or, what is about the same, as the square of the atomic weight.

For light nuclei, the surface tension energies (which give a release of energy by fusion) overshadow the effects of electric charge, so *the fusion of two light nuclei will liberate excess energy* as a by-product. However, since electric energy increases with atomic weight much faster than the surface energy does, we should expect the situation to be reversed for heavy nuclei, so that the electric charge factor is of greater importance. For these nuclei of high atomic number, we would thus expect the energy that is released by splitting the electric charge of the nucleus in two to be greater than the energy used up because of the greater surface area of the two fragments. This reasoning would lead us to predict that *excess energy will be released when a large nucleus fissions, or splits in two.*

This theoretical conclusion is in complete agreement with the empirical evidence given by the study of nuclear binding energies. Looking at Fig. 46 we notice that the value of the binding energy per particle decreases with the atomic weight for the elements in the earlier (lighter) part of the periodic system. This means that if two nuclei belonging to this region fuse together, a certain amount of nuclear energy will be set free. On the other hand, for the later (heavier) part of the periodic system the binding energy per par-

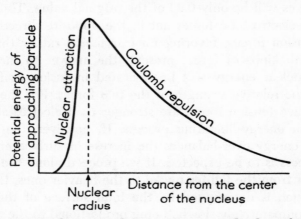

FIG. 48. *The potential energy of a positively charged particle (α-particle, proton, etc.) in the neighborhood of an atomic nucleus.*

ticle increases with increasing atomic weight, indicating that for these elements fission and not fusion will be the energy-liberating process. In between these two regions lie the elements in the neighborhood of the iron group, which have the maximum binding energy per particle and are therefore stable with respect to both fusion and fission.

Nuclear Potential Barrier

When a positively charged nuclear projectile, such as an α-particle or a proton, approaches an atomic nucleus, it is acted upon by electrostatic repulsive forces and cannot come into direct contact with the nucleus unless its kinetic energy is large enough to overcome the repulsion. However, as soon as the contact is achieved, nuclear attractive forces take hold of the approaching particle and pull it into the nucleus. Plotting the potential energy of a positively charged particle in the neighborhood of the atomic nucleus, we obtain the curve shown in Fig. 48. This curve represents a "potential barrier" for the penetration of the incident positively charged particles into the nucleus, as well as for the escape of such particles from the nucleus. According to classical mechanics, the incoming and outgoing nuclear particles can pass the potential barrier only if their kinetic energy is larger than the maximum height of the barrier. Experimental evidence shows, however, that this is definitely not so. The uranium nucleus, for example, has a radius of 9×10^{-13} cm and is surrounded by a potential barrier 27 Mev high. We would expect, therefore, that only particles having 27 Mev of potential energy or more would be able to escape from the uranium nucleus. We know, however, that α-particles emitted by uranium have an energy of only 4 Mev, and it is difficult to understand how they get out across the barrier at all. Also, in the case of the artificial transformation of elements, such as Rutherford's experiments on the bombardment of nitrogen by α-particles, the energy of the projectiles is often lower than the height of the potential barrier surrounding the bombarded nucleus; nevertheless, these projectiles penetrate into the nuclear interior, causing its disintegration.

Tunnel Effect

This paradoxical phenomenon, known as the *tunnel effect,* was explained in 1928 by G. Gamow and, independently, by R. Gurney and E. Condon, as an outcome of the wave nature of nuclear particles. In order to understand the situation, let us consider a simple example from the field of optics. A light beam falling on the interface between a dense and a light material (passing from glass into air for example), will be refracted with an angle of refraction larger than the angle of incidence. If, however, the angle of incidence exceeds a certain value, the phenomenon of "total internal reflection" will take place, and no light at all will penetrate into the second medium. This occurs because the equation:

$$\frac{\sin i}{\sin r} = \frac{1}{n} < 1$$

has no solution for r when i exceeds a certain critical value, since no angle has a sine greater than 1. If, however, we look at this phenomenon from the point of view of wave optics, we find that it is considerably more complicated than it is represented to be in geometrical optics.

Indeed, it can be shown that in the case of total internal reflection, the incident light waves are not reflected entirely from the geometrical surface separating glass and air, but penetrate into the air to a depth of several wave lengths. The lines of flow of energy for this case are shown in Fig. 49a. We see that, on passing through

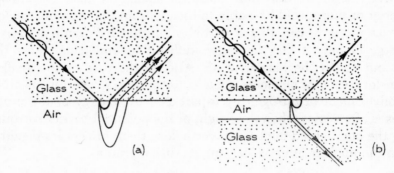

FIG. 49. *The total internal reflection of light from the glass-air interface (a), and a partial penetration into another piece of glass placed within a few wave lengths of the first one.*

the interface, the original light beam breaks into many components which penetrate into the air to different depths but always come back into the glass to form the reflected beam. This phenomenon cannot be described in terms of geometrical optics and should be considered as a peculiar case of the diffraction of light.

If we place another piece of glass right under the first one (Fig. 49b) so that the thickness of the air layer between them will be equal to only a few wave lengths, some of the light entering the air layer will reach the surface of the second piece of glass and form in it a light beam parallel to the incident beam. The intensity of that beam decreases very rapidly with increasing thickness of the air layer and becomes negligibly small when this thickness exceeds several wave lengths. Thus, wave optics explains a phenomenon which would be completely inexplicable from the point of view of classical geometrical optics.

Let us now consider a material particle with an initial energy, E, which falls on a potential barrier the height of which, U, is larger than the energy of the particle. According to classical mechanics, this particle cannot enter the region occupied by the potential barrier, since its kinetic energy within the barrier would be:

$$\tfrac{1}{2}mv^2 = E - U < 0$$

which has no real solution for v. The situation is different, however, if we consider the motion of the particle to be guided by de Broglie

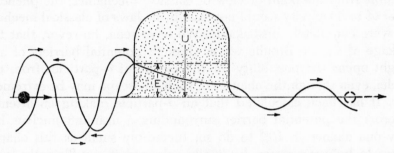

FIG. 50. A de Broglie wave falling on a potential barrier, the height of which, U, is larger than the kinetic energy, E, of the particle. The wave is partially reflected and it partially passes through.

waves; the potential barrier plays the same role for the de Broglie waves as the air layer between the two pieces of glass plays for the light waves in the case of total internal reflection. The de Broglie waves incident on a potential barrier will be partially reflected from its outer boundary while a part of them will penetrate into the barrier itself (Fig. 50). The part that penetrates into the barrier will reach its other side and will come out into the region beyond the barrier. Since the propagation of de Broglie waves guides the motion of material particles, it follows that some of the particles falling on the barrier will pass through it even though this contradicts classical mechanics. It should be noticed that the intensity of the de Broglie waves that pass through the barrier will become negligibly small if the length of the barrier exceeds several wave lengths. Since the number of particles guided by de Broglie waves is proportional to their intensity, we must conclude that the number of particles which pass through the barrier will in this case also be very small.

Alpha Decay and Nuclear Bombardment

As we mentioned before, α-particles can escape from the nuclei of radioactive elements only if they are able to pass through the nuclear potential barriers, the height of which exceeds many times the energy of escaping particles. Since such a feat is absolutely impossible from the point of view of classical mechanics, the phenomenon of radioactivity would not exist if the laws of classical mechanics were completely unshakable. We have seen, however, that the leakage of the de Broglie waves through potential barriers of any height opens the possibility for the escape of α-particles from the nuclei, even though the chances of such an escape may be extremely low. It has been calculated that an α-particle making an attempt to cross the potential barrier surrounding a uranium nucleus has only one chance in 10^{38} to do so. Incredibly small as this chance seems to be, success can be finally achieved if a sufficiently large number of attempts is made. Let us remember that the α-particles imprisoned in the nuclear interior are restlessly rushing to and fro, and constantly bouncing from the high walls of the nuclear potential barrier that surrounds them on all sides. Each time an α-particle hits the wall of its prison, it has a slight chance (one out of 10^{38}) to get out. How many such escape attempts are made per second? The velocity with which the imprisoned α-particles move inside their nuclear prison is of the order of 10^9 cm/sec, while the size of the prison is about 10^{-12} cm. By simple division, we find that an α-particle imprisoned within a nucleus collides with the surrounding walls about 10^{21} times per second. Since the chance of escape in any single collision is only one out of 10^{38}, 10^{38} escape attempts must be made altogether. At the rate of only 10^{21} attempts per second, α-particles must go on trying for $10^{38}/10^{21} = 10^{17}$ sec $= 3 \times 10^9$ years. And indeed, as we have seen before, the half lifetime of uranium nuclei is measured in billions of years.

Let us now take the case of RaC' which, in contrast to uranium, has a half-life period of only 0.0001 sec. Why does this nucleus decay so much faster? A detailed study shows that there are two reasons for it: first, the electric charge of the RaC' nucleus is smaller than that of the uranium nucleus, which reduces the height of the potential barrier through which the escaping α-particle must penetrate; secondly, the energy of α-particles from RaC' is almost twice as large as that of α-particles from uranium. Carrying out the same kind of calculations as we did in the case of the uranium nucleus, we find that an α-particle escaping from a RaC' nucleus must make only 10^{17} attempts to have a good chance to get away. At the rate of 10^{21} attempts per second, the mean waiting time for the escape reduces to $10^{17}/10^{21} = 0.0001$ sec.

Thus, we see that comparatively small variations in the height of the potential barrier and in the velocity of escaping α-particles can change the half lifetime periods from billions of years to small fractions of a second. This accounts for the great variability of the half-life periods among the radioactive elements.

What is true for the α-particles escaping from radioactive nuclei is also true for α-particles, and other positively charged atomic projectiles, that are shot at the nuclei of the ordinarily stable elements. In order to penetrate the nuclei and to cause some kind of nuclear reaction, these projectiles must first penetrate the high potential barrier surrounding the bombarded nucleus. When Rutherford bombarded nitrogen nuclei by α-particles, and when Cockcroft and Walton bombarded lithium nuclei by artificially accelerated protons, the energy of the projectiles was always smaller than the heights of the potential barriers surrounding the nuclei in question. Thus, the success of these experiments was entirely due to the quantum mechanical tunnel effect.

9. Large-Scale Nuclear Reactions

Discovery of Fission

Neutrons are the ideal projectiles for nuclear bombardment because they have no electrical charge and thus suffer no repulsion in their approach to atomic nuclei. Following the discovery of neutrons, many new types of artificial nuclear transformations have been investigated. In some cases the impact of a neutron may result in the ejection of a proton or an α-particle, as in the reactions:

$$_7N^{14} + {}_0n^1 \rightarrow {}_6C^{14} + {}_1H^1$$
$$_7N^{14} + {}_0n^1 \rightarrow {}_5B^{11} + {}_2He^4$$

In some cases the incident neutron can eject another neutron without being captured itself:

$$_6C^{12} + {}_0n^1 \rightarrow {}_6C^{11} + 2{}_0n^1$$

whereas in other cases the incident neutron can be captured by the nucleus with the release of excess energy in the form of γ-quantum. The latter process, known as the *radiative capture* of neutrons, is of particular importance for heavy nuclear targets, since in this case the ejection of protons and α-particles is strongly hindered by the "outgoing" potential barrier surrounding the nucleus. The radiative capture of the neutron leads to the formation of a heavier isotope of the bombarded element. Sometimes these isotopes are stable, so that no further nuclear transformation takes place:

$$_8O^{16} + {}_0n^1 \rightarrow {}_8O^{17} + \gamma$$

whereas in some other cases the radiative capture of a neutron leads to a β-emission:

$$_{47}Ag^{109} + {}_0n^1 \rightarrow {}_{47}Ag^{110} + \gamma$$
$$_{47}Ag^{110} \rightarrow {}_{48}Cd^{110} + e^-$$

which is necessary to re-establish the proper neutron-to-proton ratio.

In the year 1939, a German radio-chemist, Otto Hahn, with his co-worker, Fritz Strassman, studied the effect of the neutron bombardment of uranium atoms, expecting to observe the formation

FIG. 51. *Dr. Otto Hahn, who discovered that the uranium nucleus (right) when subjected to neutron bombardment breaks up into two nearly equal fragments.*

of uranium isotopes with atomic weights higher than that of ordinary uranium. To his great surprise (Fig. 51), Hahn found that the sample of uranium bombarded by neutrons contained radioactive atoms of a much lighter element, barium. The mystery of this discovery was soon cleared up by two German physicists, Lise Meitner and Otto Frisch, who suggested that in Hahn's and Strassman's experiments the nuclei of U^{238} were split by incident neutrons into two nearly equal parts:

$$_{92}U^{238} + {}_0n^1 \rightarrow {}_{56}Ba^{145} + {}_{36}Kr^{94}$$

Since the barium and krypton atoms produced in this process possessed excess neutrons, as compared with ordinary stable atoms of the same atomic weight ($_{60}Nd^{145}$ and $_{40}Zr^{94}$), these so-called fission products emitted negative electrons, making them strongly radio-active. Frisch's and Meitner's interpretation of Hahn's and Strass-man's experimental finding as the splitting of the uranium nucleus into two nearly equal parts opened new vistas in the field of nuclear physics. Instead of just "chipping off" small pieces of the bom-barded nucleus, as was the case in all previous experiments, here was a real breakup of the central body of the atom, the *fission* of a large droplet of the nuclear fluid into two half-size droplets. In-stead of just the few million electron-volts of energy observed in previous experiments on artificial nuclear transformations, uranium fission liberates 200 Mev per atom!

Detailed theoretical studies of the process of nuclear fission were carried out by Niels Bohr and John Wheeler (1911–   ) and pub-lished in the September, 1939, issue of the *Physical Review*. This was the first and last comprehensive article on the theory of nuclear fission that appeared as open literature before the security curtain was drawn tight on that subject. According to Bohr and Wheeler, the fission of heavy nuclei resulting from the impact of a neutron is a resolution of a conflict between the opposing tendencies of nuclear (attractive) and coulomb (repulsive) forces acting in the atomic nucleus. When an incident neutron (Fig. 52a) hits the nu-cleus and is absorbed by it, the excess energy communicated to the nucleus forces it to pulsate more or less as the water drops falling from the faucet do (Fig. 52c). There are two kinds of forces par-ticipating in that process.

1. The forces of nuclear surface tension (white arrows in Fig. 52c) attempting to bring the nucleus back to its original spherical shape.

2. Coulomb repulsive forces between the charges on the opposite ends of the ellipsoid attempting to break the nucleus into two halves.

In the previous chapter we have seen that the nuclear model which considers the nucleus as a positively charged droplet of uni-versal nuclear fluid leads us to conclude that for the lighter nuclei the surface tension forces have the upper hand but that for the heavier nuclei the electric forces become more and more important. Thus, we would expect that in the case of very heavy nuclei the comparatively small deformation caused by the force of a neutron

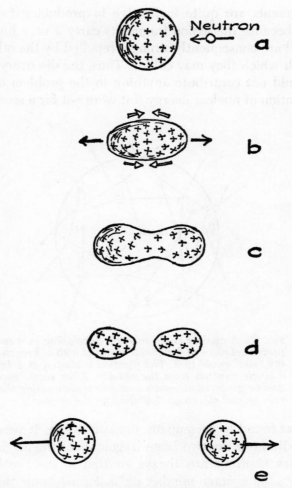

FIG. 52. *What happens when the nucleus breaks up in the fission process.*

impact may result in a breakup (fission) of the original nuclear droplet into two halves (Fig. 52c, d, e).

Fission Neutrons

In spite of the fact that each of the two fragments produced in the fission of a uranium nucleus carries about 100 Mev of energy, these fragments are quite ineffective in producing further fission processes because the fission fragments carry a very high electrical charge and are consequently strongly repelled by the other uranium nuclei with which they may collide. Thus, the discovery of uranium fission would not contribute anything to the problem of the large-scale liberation of nuclear energy if it were not for a secondary proc-

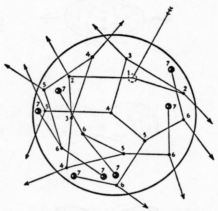

FIG. 53. *A nuclear chain reaction developing in a supercritical piece of fissionable material with a "branching ratio" equal to 2. The reaction is started at 1 by a single neutron from the outside. After seven successive generations, seven neutrons remain inside the volume and eleven are lost through the surface.*

ess that was found to accompany nuclear fission. It was discovered that, in addition to the two large fragments of the original nucleus, several extra neutrons are always emitted in the breakup. In the case of U^{235}, the average number of "fission neutrons" formed is 2.5 per uranium nucleus. These fission neutrons formed in the breakup of one uranium nucleus may collide with the surrounding uranium nuclei and produce more fission and still more fission neutrons. And, if the conditions are favorable, the breeding of fission neutrons goes *crescendo*, as does the breeding of rabbits on a rabbit farm or of fruit flies in a genetics laboratory. Thus, we get a *branching chain reaction* (Fig. 53), and in practically no time at all the nuclei of uranium in a given piece of this material break up with the liberation of a tremendous amount of energy.

Fissionable Uranium-235

As was mentioned above, natural uranium represents a mixture of two isotopes, U^{238} and U^{235}, that are present in the relative amounts of 99.3 and 0.7 per cent respectively. The study of these two isotopes under the influence of neutron bombardment had shown that the rarer isotope U^{235} is much more fissionable than the more abundant U^{238}. Indeed, whereas U^{238} nuclei do not break up unless the bombarding neutron has energy above 1.2 Mev, U^{235} nuclei can be broken up by neutrons moving with much smaller velocities, and, in fact, the breaking-up probability increases with the decreasing velocity of incident neutrons.

In the range between the high energies need to fission U^{238} and the very low, or "thermal," energies favorable for fissioning U^{235}, neutrons are absorbed by U^{238} without causing the latter to fission. Thus, the strong dilution of the active U^{235} isotope by the inactive U^{238} makes natural uranium just as useless for carrying out nuclear chain reactions as soaking wet logs are for building a campfire. Indeed, most of the fission neutrons ejected in the breakup of U^{235} nuclei in natural uranium will be captured by the much more abundant U^{238} nuclei and thus will be taken out of the game.

Accordingly, in the early stages of nuclear energy development ("Manhattan Project"), much effort was spent on the separation of the active U^{235} from the inactive U^{238}. Since the isotopes of a given element possess identical chemical properties, ordinary chemical separation methods could not be used in this case. The problem was finally solved by the development of the "diffusion separation" method, which was based on the fact that the lighter atoms of U^{235} (and their various chemical compounds) diffuse faster through tiny openings than do the heavier U^{238} atoms, and large amounts of "fissionable" uranium-235 were obtained in this way.

The Fermi-Pile and Plutonium

A good boy scout is supposed to be able to build a campfire even if the wood is soaking wet. This role of a good boy scout in the nu-

ON DECEMBER 2, 1942

MAN ACHIEVED HERE

THE FIRST SELF-SUSTAINING CHAIN REACTION

AND THEREBY INITIATED

THE CONTROLLED RELEASE OF NUCLEAR ENERGY

FIG. 54. *Enrico Fermi in front of the plaque on the wall of the University of Chicago Stadium (Stagg Field).*

clear energy project was played by the Italian-American physicist, Enrico Fermi (Fig. 54), who actually made the wet uranium logs burn. He was able to do so by utilizing the fact mentioned above, that the effectiveness of fission neutrons in producing the fission of U^{235} nuclei increases when they are slowed down. If such slowing down of fission neutrons could be achieved, the presence of in-active U^{238} would not make much difference, because very low-energy, slow neutrons are not absorbed by U^{238} to any appreciable extent. To slow down the fast fission neutrons it was necessary to use a *moderator*—i.e., some material from whose atoms the fast neutrons could bounce harmlessly and lose their energy. From considerations of conservation of momentum and energy, it can be shown that when a particle collides with another particle much less massive than itself, it is slowed down very little and loses scarcely any energy (recall the lack of effect that electrons have in deflecting α-particles). At the other extreme if a particle collides with another particle much more massive than itself, it bounces back with a speed and energy that are little changed. To be most effective, then, in helping the neutron lose energy by collision, the moderator atoms should be light atoms, comparable in size to the neutron, and should not absorb neutrons. To provide a moderator, it was decided to surround the pieces of uranium by carbon in the form of very pure graphite.

A large "pile" of graphite bricks with small pieces of natural uranium included in the structure was constructed in great secrecy under the grandstand of the University of Chicago Stadium, and on December 2, 1941, Professor A. Compton phoned to his colleague, Professor Conant of Harvard, the guarded message: "The Italian navigator has landed. The natives are friendly." This was quite correctly interpreted to mean: "Fermi's pile works successfully. The first successful nuclear chain reaction has been achieved."

In the pile, the fission chain reaction could be maintained in natural uranium, but the natural uranium was so highly diluted by carbon that high efficiency in energy production could not be achieved. Owing to the presence of inactive U^{238}, the chain reaction in the pile could not possibly develop into an efficient explosion, nor could it be very useful as a power source. So what good was the pile, except for demonstrating the purely scientific principle of the possibility of a self-maintaining nuclear reaction? Of course, the demonstration of a purely scientific principle is always of very great importance, but the pile was built at great expense in the midst of a perilous war when all expenditures were supposed to be judged on the basis of their military usefulness.

The Fermi-pile stood this acid test. Although the energy released in the fission of U^{235} nuclei could not be utilized and was literally sent down the drain by means of the water-cooling system, a new fissionable element was produced inside the pile during its operation. The neutrons that were not used in the maintenance of the chain reaction in U^{235} nuclei were captured by U^{238} nuclei, producing the heavier isotope:

$$_{92}U^{238} + _{0}n^{1} \rightarrow _{92}U^{239} + \gamma$$

Having an excess of neutrons, the nuclei of $_{92}U^{239}$ underwent two successive β-transformations, giving rise to elements with atomic numbers 93 and 94. These two elements, which do not exist in nature but have been produced artificially by human genius, were given the names *neptunium* and *plutonium*. The reactions following the neutron capture by U^{238} can be written:

$$_{92}U^{239} \rightarrow _{93}Np^{239} + e^{-}$$
$$_{93}Np^{239} \rightarrow _{94}Pu^{239} + e^{-}$$

Being chemically different from uranium, the plutonium produced in the Fermi-pile can be separated and purified with much less effort than it takes to separate a light uranium isotope from the heavy one, and this element turned out to be even more fissionable than U^{235}. In fact, whereas U^{235} gives rise to 2.5 fission neutrons, the corresponding figure for Pu^{239} is 2.7 fission neutrons.

Critical Size

When a single fission process occurs inside a given sample of pure U^{235} or Pu^{239}, several fission neutrons are ejected from the point where the nuclear breakup took place. The average distance a fission neutron must travel through the material before it is slowed down to the point where it can effectively cause a fission reaction is about 10 cm, so that if the size of the sample in question is less than that, most of the fission neutrons will cross the surface of the sample and fly away before they have a chance to cause another fission and produce more neutrons. Thus, no progressive chain reaction can develop if the sample of fissionable material is too small. Going to larger and larger samples, we find that more and more fission neutrons produced in the interior have a chance to produce another fission by colliding with a nucleus before they escape through the surface, and for samples of a very large size only a small fraction of the neutrons produced in them has a chance to reach the surface before fissioning one of the nuclei. The size of the sample of a given fissionable material for which the percentage of neutrons giving rise to subsequent fission processes is high enough to secure a progressive chain reaction is known as the *critical size* for that particular material. Since the number of neutrons per fission is larger in the case of plutonium than in the case of U^{235}, the critical size of plutonium samples is smaller than that of U^{235} samples because the former can afford larger losses of neutrons through its surface.

Nuclear Reactors

As we have just seen, a sample of fissionable material smaller than the "critical size" is unable to carry on a nuclear chain reaction. If the size of the sample is *exactly critical*, the number of neutrons produced in each generation is the same as that produced in the previous one, resulting in steady nuclear energy liberation. The original Fermi-pile and its later modifications maintain nuclear reactions at the critical size level. It must be mentioned in this connection that the conditions of "criticality" are extremely unstable: a small deviation in one direction will result in the rapid extinction of fission neutrons and the cut-off of the nuclear chain reaction, whereas a deviation in another direction will lead to a rapid multiplication of the fission neutrons and the melting of the entire structure. Thus, the important problem in maintaining a steady chain reaction is that of regulating the rate of neutron production and of keeping the chain reaction from dying out or running away. This is achieved by using control rods made from neutron-absorbing materials (such as boron) which are automatically pushed in or pulled out from narrow channels drilled through the reacting fissionable material as soon as the rate of neutron production drops below or exceeds the desired level.

Many Fermi-piles are unsuitable for purposes of nuclear power production because of the high dilution of uranium by carbon; they should be considered rather as plants in which plutonium is produced. Because they can produce more fissionable material (Pu^{239})

than they consume (U^{235}), this type of pile is sometimes called a *breeder reactor*. For the purpose of nuclear power production, we can use controlled nuclear chain reactions in relatively pure fissionable materials, such as U^{235} or Pu^{239}, which can be run at high temperatures. In the "swimming pool" reactor, in which several cylindrical containers filled with pure fissionable material are placed at

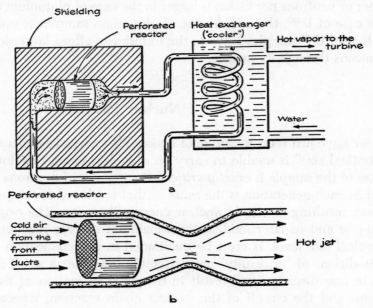

FIG. 55. *Two types of nuclear reactors for propulsion purposes: (a) a closed-cycle reactor and (b) an open-cycle reactor.*

the bottom of a large water tank, the water circulating through the tank carries away the heat produced in the fission process and also protects the observer from the deadly nuclear radiation. The water emits a ghostly blue glow as a result of what is called *Cherenkoff radiation*, after the Russian physicist who first analyzed the phenomeon in 1934. For this, and related work, Cherenkoff received the 1958 Nobel Prize in Physics. Cherenkoff radiation is produced by two separate effects that we have previously become acquainted with: the Compton effect and shock waves. We have spoken of the Compton effect before, primarily in terms of the scattering of an X-ray photon and its consequent loss of energy because of collision with an electron. In the reactor tank, high-energy γ-photons interacting with electrons send the electrons flying off at speeds greater than the speed of light in the water. The result is similar to the bow wave of a ship traveling through water faster than the surface ripples can spread out: a shock wave (a bow wave for the ship) is formed. Analysis beyond the scope of this book shows that this electromagnetic shock wave will give rise to the blue Cherenkoff radiation.

In Fig. 54a and b we give the schemes of two different types of *nuclear power reactors*. In both cases the block of fissionable material is perforated by long cylindrical channels for the passage of the "working fluid" that receives and carries out the heat produced in the fission process. Scheme (a) is known as a *closed-cycle nuclear reactor* since in it the working fluid (a molten light metal) is continuously circulating between the reactor and the "cooler," where the heat is used to produce water vapor for the operation of an ordinary steam turbine. This type of nuclear power reactor is installed, for example, in the "Nautilus," the first nuclear-powered submarine of the U. S. Navy. Figure 55b is an *open-cycle nuclear reactor* which is likely to become very useful for the propulsion of nuclear-powered jet planes. In this type of power reactor, the air coming in through the intake ducts in front of the airplane is heated to a high temperature while passing through the reactor and is ejected, in the form of a fast jet, through the nozzle at the rear.

Fission Bombs

If the sample of fissionable material exceeds the critical mass, the number of fission neutrons and the rate of energy production will increase exponentially with time, and the process will acquire an explosive nature. The principle of the fission bomb, or the "atomic bomb" as it is commonly called, consists of building up (assembling) a highly supercritical mass of fissionable material in such a short time period that the nuclear energy liberation that starts at the beginning of the assembly period does not develop to any important degree before the assembly job is finished. This can be accomplished in a simple way by inserting one subcritical piece of fissionable material into another subcritical piece as indicated in Fig. 56. In order to perform the assembly process fast enough, we must shoot the inserted piece at a high speed from a gun muzzle, which earned for this assembly method the name of "gun gadget." There are also other more ingenious methods of bringing a given amount of fissionable material to supercritical size.

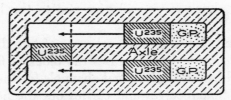

FIG. 56. *The principle of the gun-type atomic bomb. The ignition of gunpowder (G.P.) shoots a U-235 cylinder along the axle and places it around another part of U-235, which forms the left end of the axle.*

The energy liberation in the explosion of nuclear bombs is measured, according to established convention, in units known as *kilotons* and *megatons,* which refer to the weight of TNT (ordinary high explosive) that liberates the same amount of energy. One kiloton, i.e., the energy liberated in the explosion of 1,000 tons of TNT, equals 5×10^{19} erg or about 10^{12} calories.

Thermonuclear Reactions

In experiments on the artificial transformation of light elements by electrically accelerated charged particles, one gets extremely low yields of nuclear reactions. The reason for this is that the charged nuclear projectiles, such as protons or α-particles, rapidly lose their energy on the ionization of the material through which they fly, and only a very few of them (about 0.01 per cent) have a chance to collide with a nucleus of the bombarded element before spending all their energy on tearing off atomic electrons. Thus, whereas the nuclear reactions that are caused by the high-energy projectiles produced in various kinds of high-voltage particle accelerators are extremely valuable for the study of nuclear properties, they are completely worthless for the purpose of large-scale nuclear energy liberation.

The most natural way of producing nuclear reactions in light elements on a large scale is the good old chemical method of raising the temperature of the reacting substances. Although in ordinary chemical reactions a temperature of only a few hundred degrees may be quite sufficient to induce reactions between the colliding molecules, nuclear reactions require temperatures of many millions of degrees. At these temperatures, the atoms are completely dissociated into bare nuclei and free electrons, and the kinetic energy of thermal motion becomes high enough to overcome the electrostatic repulsion between the charges of the colliding nuclei. As in the case of nuclear bombardment by artificially accelerated particles, the energy of thermal motion does not need to exceed the height of the potential barrier separating the colliding nuclei, and penetration can occur by virtue of the tunnel effect for much lower energies. Whenever two colliding nuclei come into bodily contact, various types of fusion reactions may take place, and the nuclear energy flows out in a steady stream. These types of nuclear reactions, which are induced by the violent thermal collisions between the nuclei of the substance subjected to very high temperature, are known as *thermonuclear reactions,* and are responsible for the energy production in the interior of the sun and in other stars in the universe. The principal thermonuclear reaction responsible for the energy production in the sun and stars is a transformation of hydrogen into helium according to the formula:

$$4_1H^1 = {}_2He^4 + 25.7 \text{ Mev}$$

However, even at the temperature of 20 million degrees in the solar interior, this reaction goes very slowly, liberating only 10^{-5} cal/gm/sec. The reason why our sun is so hot is that this meager heat produced by the thermonuclear reaction accumulates within its giant body before it has a chance to be radiated from the surface.

In man's search for thermonuclear reactions, he uses the faster-burning, heavier isotopes of hydrogen, deuterium ($_1H^2$ or D), which occurs in nature, and tritium ($_1H^3$ or T), which is nearly non-existent in nature and must be produced by nuclear reaction processes.

All possible reactions between these two isotopes are summarized below:

$$_1D^2 + {}_1D^2 \rightarrow {}_2He^3 + n + 3.25 \text{ Mev}$$
$$_1D^2 + {}_1D^2 \rightarrow {}_1T^3 + {}_1H^1 + 4 \text{ Mev}$$
$$_1D^2 + {}_1T^3 \rightarrow {}_2He^4 + n + 17.6 \text{ Mev}$$

These reactions go very fast even at "moderately low" temperatures. In Fig. 57 we give the calculated rate of energy production in the D-D reaction. A similar curve can be constructed for the D-T reaction, which would run somewhat above the D-D curve. We see

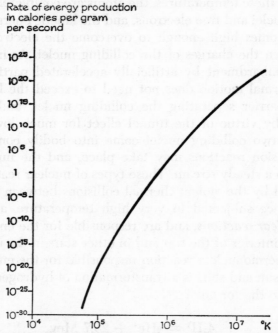

FIG. 57. *The calculated rate of thermonuclear energy production in deuterium (at liquid density) for different temperatures.*

that, while at 10^5°K this energy production is negligibly small, at a temperature of only 10^6°K it rises to 1,000 cal/gm/sec, which corresponds to about 5 horsepower for each kg of material. At a temperature of 10^7°K the reaction rate rises to 10^{18} cal/gm/sec and all of the material will be consumed within a microsecond. This almost instantaneous release of nuclear energy leads to an explosion and is used in the construction of hydrogen bombs. However, to start the explosion one has first to heat the material to the required high temperature, which can be done by using the ordinary uranium bomb as a starter. Notice here that the efficiency of such a thermonuclear bomb can be considerably increased by surrounding it with a layer of ordinary (cheap) uranium. In fact, although no fission chain reaction can be maintained in ordinary uranium, the numerous neu-trons released by a thermonuclear reaction will cause individual fissions of uranium nuclei and add to the total energy release. Of course, such a design will result in the production of very large amounts of fission products, which will contaminate a wide area around the explosion and will be distributed by winds all over the globe.

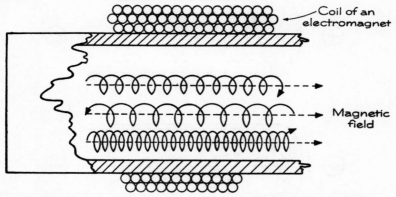

FIG. 58. *Magnetic confinement, showing charged particles circling along the magnetic lines in a tube. The direction of motion and the "step" of spirals are determined by the horizontal component of the particles' velocity and are not influenced by the field.*

If, instead of having a violent explosion, we prefer to run a con-trolled thermonuclear reaction at a steady low rate, the physical conditions under which such a reaction can take place must be dras-tically changed. First of all, the reaction should be run at *extremely low gas densities,* since otherwise the pressure of the gas at the re-quired temperatures of a few hundred thousand degrees will rise to millions of atmospheres and no walls will be able to contain it. Secondly, this rarefied gas *must somehow be kept away from the walls of the vessel,* since otherwise the process of heat conduction into the walls will rapidly reduce the temperature of the gas below the minimum value required for thermonuclear reactions. This can be achieved in several different ways, all of which are based essen-tially on the use of strong magnetic fields. At the very high tempera-tures required in this case, the deuterium gas in the tube will be completely ionized and will consist entirely of negatively charged electrons and positively charged deuterons. (This state of matter is described nowadays by the term "plasma.") We know that when an electrically charged particle moves through a magnetic field, it experiences a force perpendicular to the direction of its motion and to that of the field. This force compels the particles to spiral along the direction of the magnetic lines, as shown in Fig. 58. Thus, by forming a strong axial magnetic field in a tube, we can effectively prevent

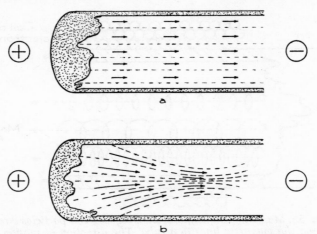

FIG. 59. The "pinch effect." (a) An electric current through the tube can be considered as a bunch of parallel "elementary" currents; (b) when the strength of the current is suddenly increased, the magnetic attraction between the "elementary" currents causes the "pinch effect."

free deuterons and tritons from coming close to the walls. If this can be achieved, the collisions between the particles spiraling along the tube are expected to result in D-D or D-T reactions with the release of nuclear energy and of large amounts of neutrons. Of course, in order to start such a process the gas in the tube must first be heated to a very high temperature by some outside agent.

The second possibility consists in using magnetic forces caused by short but strong electric discharges through the tube. Two parallel electric currents flowing in the same direction are magnetically attracted toward each other so that, in the case of a sufficiently strong current, the gas (or rather the plasma) inside the tube will have a tendency to detach itself from the walls and to be squeezed into a narrow jet along the axis. How this so-called pinch effect operates can be understood by inspecting Fig. 59a and b. In contrast to the previously described method, the pinch-effect device operates in jerks, as an automobile engine does, but it has the advantage that the gas in the tube is automatically heated by the electric discharge, and no outside heating is needed. It has been estimated that a current of several hundred thousand amperes lasting for a few microseconds would produce a "pinch" strong enough to cause a thermonuclear reaction in deuterium. Work in the above-described directions is being carried out now in many laboratories of the world, and it is entirely possible that the problem of controlled thermonuclear reactions will be solved before this book comes off press.

10. Mystery
Particles

The Elusive Neutrino

In addition to protons and neutrons, which form the nuclei of atoms, and electrons, which form their outer envelopes, physicists have discovered a whole array of other particles. These, although not permanent constituent parts of the nuclei, nonetheless play an important role in their properties.

Early studies of radioactive beta decay (the emission of an electron by an unstable atomic nucleus) led to the conclusion that something was wrong with the energy balance involved. Whereas alpha particles emitted by a given radioactive element always carry a well-defined amount of energy characteristic of that element, beta particles from one radioactive element show a wide energy spread, ranging from almost zero up to high-energy values. Since the total energy liberation in the transformation of one atomic nucleus into another is expected to be the same for all nuclei of a given kind, it was suspected that another particle must be coming out of the nucleus, along with the electron and this carried away the missing balance of energy. This hypothetical particle, which must be electrically neutral and must be considerably lighter than the electron (we still do not know how light it is), received the name *neutrino,* which means "little neutral" in Italian. Their absence of electric charge and their extremely small mass allow neutrinos to penetrate thick material layers with the greatest of ease, and a heavy concrete wall is just as ineffective in stopping a beam of neutrinos as a chicken fence is in stopping a swarm of mosquitoes. In fact, it can be computed on the basis of theoretical considerations that, in order to stop a beam of neutrinos effectively, one would need a shield several light-years thick! Thus, the neutrinos produced in various nuclear transformations could escape unobserved with their loads of energy, frustrating the physicists and causing discrepancies in the balance of the records of incoming and outgoing energy. But, whenever there is a suspicion of a new unkown particle, physicists are as good as Canadian Mounties in getting their man, and the nets were gradually drawn close around the elusive neutrino.

The first experimental evidence of the existence of neutrinos, which were originally introduced as purely hypothetical particles, was provided by the observation of the recoil of the nuclei from which the neutrinos were emitted. The unstable isotope of beryllium, Be^7, which can be produced artificially by means of nuclear bombardment, emits a positive electron and is transformed into the stable isotope of lithium, Li^7, according to the following equation, in which v represents a neutrino:

$$_4Be^7 \rightarrow {}_3Li^7 + e^+ + v$$

Instead of this decay, however, another reaction can occur, in which the Be^7 nucleus is transformed into a Li^7 nucleus by capturing one of the electrons from the inner (K) electron shell of the atom:

$$_4Be^7 + (e^-)_{\text{atomic}} \longrightarrow {}_3Li^7 + v'$$

Indeed, the addition of a negative charge to a nucleus is equivalent to the loss of a positive charge. Since the captured negative electron belongs to the original unstable atom, all that happens here is the emission of a neutrino and, through the conservation of momentum, the recoil of the atom from which it came. Since the neutrino does not produce any visible track in the cloud chamber, it looks as if the Be^7 atom started suddenly to move by itself without any agent responsible for the move. It reminds one of an incident in an H. G. Wells story, "The Invisible Man," in which a self-respecting British bobby was suddenly catapulted forward by a kick in the pants while there was apparently nobody behind him. This phenomenon was actually observed in a cloud chamber containing unstable Be^7 atoms, and gave the first supporting evidence for the existence of neutrinos.

But the acid test of the neutrino hypothesis came in the attempt to stop the escaping neutrinos in their tracks. And, in spite of the almost incredible ability of neutrinos to make their getaway, physicists managed in 1955 to stop a few of them, thus finding unquestionable proof of their existence. F. Reines and C. Cowan of the Los Alamos Scientific Laboratory used for this purpose the collision process between neutrinos and protons in which the neutrino is expended to produce a positive electron and to transform the proton into a neutron:

$$p + \text{neutrino} \rightarrow n + e^+$$

These two scientists built a giant particle counter that registers neutrons as well as electrons and placed it near one of the nuclear piles at the Savannah River Nuclear Energy Project. The nuclear reactions taking place in the operating pile produce a tremendous number of neutrinos that stream out through a heavy shielding which holds back all other nuclear radiations. Although the chance of a neutrino hitting a proton and producing the above-mentioned reaction is only 1 out of 10^{30}, some of these reactions do actually take place, resulting in the simultaneous appearance of a neutron and the accompanying positive electron. Thus, the uncatchable neutrino was finally caught and joined the company of well-established elementary particles.

Mesons

The next member to enter the growing family of auxiliary nuclear particles was also born as the result of purely theoretical considerations. In 1935 a Japanese theoretical physicist, Hidekei Yukawa (known as "Headache" Yukawa to students who struggle with his mathematics), proposed a new particle which would account for the strong forces binding neutrons and protons together in the nucleus.

Probably the best way to picture a force of attraction between two bodies caused by the presence of a third body is to imagine two hungry dogs who come into possession of a juicy bone and are grabbing it from each other to take a bite. The tasty bone is continuously passing from the jaws of one of them into the jaws of the other, and in the resulting struggle, the two dogs become inseparably locked. Yukawa's idea was that attractive forces between the nucleons (the collective name for neutrons and protons) are due to a similar struggle for the possession of that new tasty particle. That

FIG. 60. *The exchange of a neutral meson between a proton (left) and a neutron (right).*

new particle could be electrically neutral or could carry a positive
or negative charge, and the exchange process is similar to that shown
in Fig. 60.

The binding energy between two nucleons, due to the periodic
exchange of Yukawa's new particle between them, is hv (as it is usual
in all oscillation processes) where v is the frequency of exchange.
Since, according to the experimental data, this energy is about 10^{-4}
erg, we conclude that

$$v = \frac{10^{-4}}{10^{-27}} = 10^{23} \text{ per second}$$

Neutrons and protons must have a very large appetite for this
Japanese food if they fight so intensively for its possession!

According to Yukawa's theoretical considerations, the new particles must have a mass intermediate between that of protons and
that of electrons, so they received the name *mesons* (from the Greek
mesos meaning "between").

Two years after the introduction of these purely hypothetical particles for the explanation of nuclear forces, mesons were actually
observed in cosmic rays by an America physicist, Carl Anderson.
The so-called primary cosmic rays bombarding the atmosphere of
our planet are streams of extremely high-energy protons and a few
other heavier positively charged nuclei that are probably accelerated by electromagnetic fields in interstellar space. The energies of
these particles range from comparatively low values to thousands
of billions of electron-volts. Colliding with the nuclei of atmospheric
oxygen and nitrogen at the outer fringes of the atmosphere, these
primary cosmic ray particles produce various kinds of penetrating
radiations, including high-energy γ-quanta and streams of negative
and positive electrons; in fact, as was mentioned earlier, positive
electrons were first discovered in cosmic rays. Observing the tracks
formed by cosmic ray particles in a cloud chamber placed between
the poles of a strong magnet, Anderson noticed that the trajectories
of some of the particles, both positively and negatively charged,
were bent by a magnetic field more than would be expected in the
case of fast protons but considerably less than should be the case
with electrons. From the observed magnetic deflection, Anderson
estimated that this new kind of particle was about 200 times heavier

than an electron, which was in agreement with Yukawa's theoretical prediction. The behavior of the new particles, however, in their reluctance to react with nucleons, made it very doubtful that these were the predicted exchange-force particles. Ten years later the British physicist, C. F. Powell, demonstrated that there are two kinds of mesons: the π-meson (called "pion") which is produced at the upper fringes of the atmosphere by primary cosmic rays, and the μ-meson (or "muon") into which the pion spontaneously decays on its way down in about 10^{-8} sec after being formed.

$$\pi^{\pm} \rightarrow \mu^{\pm} + \text{neutrino}$$

Muons, or μ-mesons, have been detected by cloud chambers in relatively large numbers at the surface of the earth, and investigations have shown them to have a half-life of 10^{-6} sec, decaying into an electron and two neutrinos, according to the equation:

$$\mu^{\pm} \rightarrow e^{\pm} + 2\nu$$

According to Einstein's theory of relativity, 3×10^{10} cm/sec is the absolute speed limit for any material particle. Even at this speed, which is the speed of light, the muon would require 10^{-3} sec to reach the earth's surface. If the mean lifetime of a muon is only 10^{-6} sec, how does it manage to survive the journey?

The answer to this question comes from the same relativity theory that enforces the speed limit. From our point of view, the watch of a swiftly moving observer will lose time; relative to us, the muon is traveling at enormously high speed, and the "watch" that times its life appears to us to be running slowly. In fact, the cosmic ray muons travel at a speed so near the speed of light that time is expanded by a factor of many thousands, and what we measure as a thousandth of a second will be to the muon much less than its lifetime of a millionth of a second. Besides explaining the survival of the muon, the above argument serves as another strong proof of the theory of relativity. Both pions and muons can carry either a positive or a negative electric charge (π^{+}, π^{-}, μ^{+}, μ^{-}), and in addition there also exist neutral pions (π^{0}). All of these new particles, as well as the positive and negative cosmic ray electrons (e^{+}, e^{-}), form a sequence somewhat similar to the sequence of the radioactive elements. It is now established that the primary high-energy (positive)

protons entering the outer fringes of the atmosphere also give rise
to neutral pions. Neutral pions possess a very short lifetime (about

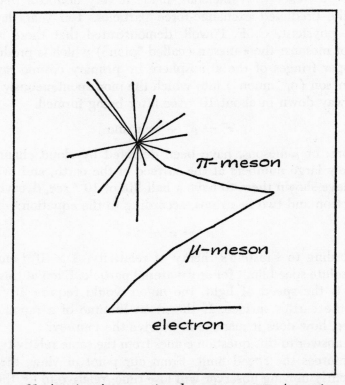

FIG. 61. *A series of consecutive elementary events. A cosmic ray
proton hits an atomic nucleus (upper left) in a photographic
emulsion and produces a burst of many different fragments (the
so-called cosmic ray star). One of the particles, a heavy meson
(or pion), travels a long way and, at the right edge of the drawing, breaks up into a light meson (or muon) and a neutrino, the
trajectory of which is not shown in the drawing. The muon travels
to the lower left corner and breaks up in turn into two neutrinos
(their tracks are not shown) and an electron, which travels to the
right.*

10^{-16} sec) and, in spite of their high velocity, break up into two
γ-quanta:

$$\pi^0 \rightarrow \gamma + \gamma'$$

long before reaching the surface of the earth. Positive, negative,
and neutral pions interact very strongly with atomic nuclei and are

apparently the particles introduced hypothetically by Yukawa for explanation of nuclear forces.

For the study of pions and their decay, photographic equipment attached to large balloons must be sent high into the stratosphere. Since cloud chamber equipment is too bulky and heavy to be sent up in balloons, cosmic ray researchers have developed a new method for photographing the tracks of cosmic particles at high altitudes. Instead of using the ionizing properties of fast charged particles passing through humid air, the new method is based on the fact that these particles affect the grains through which they pass when they travel through a fine-grained photographic emulsion. When the photographic plate is developed, it shows dark streaks that correspond to the trajectories followed by the particles. A sketch of a very rare photograph of this kind showing the formation of a pion resulting from the collision of a primary cosmic ray particle with a composite nucleus and the subsequent decay of this pion into a muon and an electron is shown in Fig. 61. After the development of the Bevatron and Cosmatron, it became possible to produce pions in the laboratory and this considerably accelerated the progress of the study of their properties.

More and More Particles

Following the discovery of pions and muons, other particles began to turn up. They appeared in cosmic ray studies and in experiments with new high-energy particle accelerators. Some of these particles (the K mesons) are intermediate in mass between electrons and nucleons, while others (Λ, Σ, Ξ particles) are more massive than nucleons and are known as *hyperons*. Table 6 lists all the particles reported at the date of the conclusion of this manuscript, giving their masses, lifetimes, and modes of decay.

We do not know whether all the particles listed in the table are really elementary or whether some of them are formed by the combination of others. The experimental and theoretical studies of this problem represent the frontier of today's physics, and the solution will lead to a much deeper understanding of the nature of the physical world we live in.

What Lies Ahead?

As described at the beginning of this book, ancient Greek philosophers, who conceived the idea of ultimate structural units of matter, recognized four kinds of atoms: those of stone, of water, of air, and of fire. The subsequent development of chemistry brought

TABLE 6

THE PROPERTIES OF THE ELEMENTARY PARTICLES OF MATTER

(Bold type indicates the particles known before 1930)

Name and symbol	Mass (in electron masses)	Mean lifetime (in seconds)	Decay Scheme
Xi $\Xi^\pm$	2,585	10^{-10}	$\Lambda^0 + \pi^\pm$
Sigma $\Sigma^\pm$	2,330	10^{-10}	$n + \pi^\pm$
Lambda Λ^0	2,182	2.7×10^{-10}	$p + \pi^-$ or $n + p^+$
Neutron n	1,838.6	10^3	$p^\pm + e^\mp + \nu$
Proton p$^\pm$	1,836.1	stable	
K-meson $K^\pm$	966.5	10^{-8}	$\pi^\pm + \pi^0 + \pi^0$ etc.
K-meson K^0	965	10^{-10}	$\pi^0 + \pi^0$ or $\pi^+ + \pi^-$
Pion $\pi^\pm$	273.2	2.6×10^{-8}	$\mu^\pm + \nu$
Pion π^0	264.2	10^{-16}	two gamma rays
Muon $\mu^\pm$	206.7	2.2×10^{-6}	$e^\pm + 2\nu$
Electron e$^\pm$	1	stable	
Neutrino ν	0	stable	

the number of different atomic species to 92, but up to the end of the nineteenth century chemists and physicists were still subscribing to Democritus' dogma that the atoms of various chemical elements cannot be divided into still smaller parts. The work of Sir J. J. Thomson, Lord Rutherford, and other scientists who were digging into the atomic interior, proved, however, that the indivisibility of atoms is a myth and that, indeed, the atoms and their nuclei are

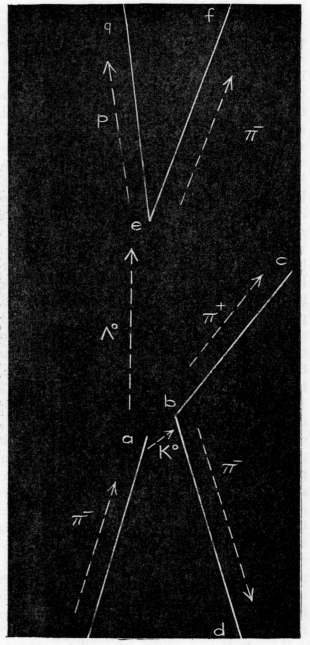

FIG. 62. *The leapfrog game of elementary particles photographed by liquid hydrogen bubble chamber at the Lawrence Radiation Laboratory of the University of California. A negative pion, entering from the lower right corner, gives rise at point a to a neutral Λ-particle traveling upwards (no visible track) and a neutral K-meson travelling to the left (no visible track). At point e, Λ°-particle produces a proton and a negative pion travelling to points g and f. At point b, K°-meson produces a pair of positive and negative pions travelling to points c and d.*

extremely complex systems built from much smaller units which we now call *elementary particles*. First, the number of elementary particles was limited to two—*protons* and *electrons*—later joined by *neutrons*, which were considered to be just ordinary protons that had lost their electric charge. But soon hordes of new particles with the claim of elementarity began showering down on the heads of the physicists. They were *neutrinos*, much lighter than an electron; several kinds of *mesons*, with masses between that of an electron and a proton; and *hyperons*, which exceed the proton mass. To each of these particles corresponds an *anti-particle* which can be annihilated in an encounter with a "normal" particle, the entire mass of both particles being turned into the quanta of radiant energy. More recently, physicists got into trouble with what can be called *mirror particles*. Everybody knows that, looking at a mirror image of the right hand, one appears to see the left hand, and vice versa. Since both right and left hands actually exist in reality, the "through-the-looking-glass" world coincides with the real world. Until recently, it was believed that the same is true in the world of elementary particles, that one can always find a real particle identical with the mirror image of another one. This dogma was known as the *conservation of parity*, a term referring to the symmetry properties of the equations describing physical phenomena. In 1957, however, two Chinese-American theoretical physicists, Chen Ning Yang and Tsung Dao Lee, concluded that, although conservation of parity undoubtedly holds for such phenomena as the emission of electromagnetic waves, it may not hold for the decay of elementary particles. Consider, for example, the transformation of a neutron into a proton with the emission of an electron. Protons and neutrons possess what is known as *spin* which may be interpreted as the result of their rapid rotation around the axes, and the emission of electrons is expected to take place along this rotation-axis. How is the direction in which the electron flies out of a neutron correlated with the direction of a neutron's rotation? One possibility would be that there is no correlation, that the electron could fly with equal probabilities in either of the two directions (i.e., either from the North Pole or from the South Pole, if we compare the rotation of a neutron with the rotation of the earth around its axis).

If we have two neutrons (*a* and *b* in Fig. 63*a*) spinning in the same direction, say clockwise, but emitting electrons in opposite directions, their mirror images will appear to us as a' and b' in the same figure. But b' is identical with a turned upside down, and a' is identical with upside-down b. Thus the parity principle is fulfilled.

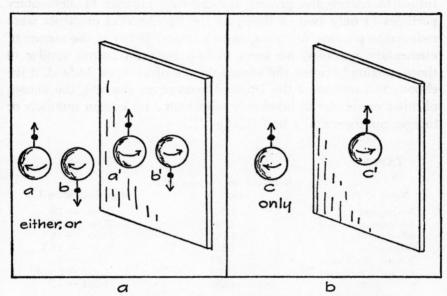

FIG. 63. *Conservation (a) and nonconservation (b) of purity. In (a) the mirror images of* a *and* b *can be transformed into* b *and* a *by simply turning them upside down. In (b), where the emission of an electron is coupled with the rotation of the neutron in a unique way, the mirror image does not exist in the real world.*

But if we assume that an electron is always emitted in only one definite direction in respect to the rotation of the neutron (only through the North Pole in our terrestrial analogy), the mirror image (Fig. 62b) does not correspond to any real case of neutron decay and the parity principle is violated. Direct experiments with the beta decay of radioactive nuclei (which is due to the decay of neutrons in their interior) and also with the decay of mesons, have proved, however, that that is exactly what happens. Thus, it seems, that the world of elementary particles is lopsided, with one half of it missing, and nobody knows why.

The world of elementary particles occupies the attention of physicists today, just as the world of atoms occupied it a few decades ago. Are these "elementary particles" really elementary in the good old Democritian sense of the word? Why do they have these particular masses, and why do they go through these particular transformations, with these particular rates? Will it be possible in the future to reduce the present fast-growing number of elementary particles to only two or three, as the 92 chemical elements were reduced to protons, neutrons, and electrons? Between the masses of elementary particles, we seem to find certain relations similar to those existing between the atomic weight of isotopes. Indeed, if we choose as a unit mass the 137-fold mass of an electron, the masses of other particles will be closely represented by integer numbers or integer numbers and a half (Table 7).

TABLE 7

Name of particle	Measured mass in respect to electron	Mass divided by 137
Ξ—hyperon	2,585	$18.88 \rightarrow 19$
Σ—hyperon	2,330	$17.02 \rightarrow 17$
Λ^0—hyperon	2,182	$15.95 \rightarrow 16$
nucleon	1,837	$13.41 \rightarrow 13.5$
$K^\pm$ and K^0—meson	965	$7.05 \rightarrow 7$
$\pi^\pm$ and π^0—meson	268	$1.954 \rightarrow 2$
$\mu^\pm$—meson	206	$1.504 \rightarrow 1.5$

The number 137 is not chosen at random but is a famous dimensionless physical constant equal to the product of quantum constant multiplied by the velocity of light divided by the square of elementary charge. In spite of numerous attempts, particularly those made by Sir Arthur Eddington, nobody knows why this ratio is 137 and not some other number.

One may say that the present opinion that elementary particles will really bear out their name (as the atoms did not) is due to our comparatively slight familiarity with their properties, and that all of them will be found in future to be as complex as grand pianos. It may also be that this will not be the end of the road and that years later much smaller "subelementary" particles will be discovered. There is no way to predict the future, and the question whether Democritus' original philosophical concept of indivisibility was right or wrong will never be answered by empirical means. But somehow many scientists, including the author, feel happier with the thought that, in the study of matter, "things will come to an end" and that the physicists of the future will know all there is to know about the inner structure of matter. And it also seems quite plausible that the elementary particles of modern physics really deserve their name, because their properties and behavior appear to be much simpler than could ever be said about the atom.

Index